Poems From
Southern Scotland
Edited by Annabel Cook

 Young**Writers**

First published in Great Britain in 2008 by:
Young Writers
Remus House
Coltsfoot Drive
Peterborough
PE2 9JX
Telephone: 01733 890066
Website: www.youngwriters.co.uk

SB ISBN 978-1 84431 442 3

Foreword

Young Writers was established in 1991 and has been passionately devoted to the promotion of reading and writing in children and young adults ever since. The quest continues today. Young Writers remains as committed to the nurturing of poetic and literary talent as ever.

This year's Young Writers competition has proven as vibrant and dynamic as ever and we are delighted to present a showcase of the best poetry from across the UK and in some cases overseas. Each poem has been selected from a wealth of *Little Laureates* entries before ultimately being published in this, our sixteenth primary school poetry series.

Once again, we have been supremely impressed by the overall quality of the entries we have received. The imagination, energy and creativity which has gone into each young writer's entry made choosing the poems a challenging and often difficult but ultimately hugely rewarding task - the general high standard of the work submitted ensured this opportunity to bring their poetry to a larger appreciative audience.

We sincerely hope you are pleased with this final collection and that you will enjoy *Little Laureates Poems From Southern Scotland* for many years to come.

Contents

Scott Miller (7)   16
Nelson Lissanon   17
Shawna Philipsen   17
Maya Coates (7)   17
Nicola Cringean (7)   18
Corann Henderson (7)   18
Stan Ashcroft (7)   18
Elisabeth Meredith (6)   19
Craig Percy (7)   19
Lucie Morren   19
Megan Grant (7)   19
Julia Laughland (7)   20
Tamsin Brass Brogan (7)   20
Aidan Cranna (6)   20
Nathan Wilson (7)   20
Daniel Skiffington (7)   21

Capshard Primary School, Kirkcaldy
Christopher Mitchell (10)   21
Ashley Walton (11)   21
Rebekah Bowie (10)   22
Holly Armour (11)   22
Louise Hannah (11)   23
Shaun Gilmour (10)   23
Stephanie Campbell (10)   23
Scott Thomson (10)   24
Daniel Nugent (10)   24
Megan Stevenson (10)   25
Scott Binnie (10)   25
Hannah McGowan (10)   26
Hannah Whyte (10)   26
Sarah Louden (10)   27
Michael Duncan (10)   27
Amy Mearns (10)   27
Rachel Livingston (10)   28

Cummertrees Primary School, Annan
Georgina Coyle (11)   28
James Crichton (11)   29
Jennifer Hamilton (10)   29
Kieran Saunders (10)   29

Connor Brown (9)	30
Andrew Watret (11)	30
Louise Maclean (10)	30
Niall Goldie (11)	31
Mhairi Macgregor (10)	31
Abigail Christie (9)	32
Molly Adams (10)	32
Mary Padgett (9)	33
Rachel Widdowson (9)	33
Fraser Bell (10)	33
Rebecca Hamilton (9)	34
Robert Broatch (11)	34
Emily Padgett (10)	34
Katie Dale (10)	35

Currie Primary School, Currie

Lucy Ritchie (10)	35
Cade Kirk (10)	36
Ronan Sinclair (10)	36
Darragh Spence (10)	37
Callum Johnston (10)	37
Dane Anderson (10)	38
Duncan Brown (10)	38
Caitlin Summers (11)	39
Bryce Ricketts (11)	39
Caitlin Fraser (11)	40
Jessica Speake (11)	41
Rhian Ferrigan (11)	42
Nikita Tilak (11)	43
Lipika Chowdhury (11)	44
Olivia Burgess (10)	44
Valerie Cronshaw (11)	45
Victoria McCann (11)	45
Caitlin Treschman (10)	46
Alix Dobbie (11)	47
Beth Sutherland (11)	48
Rachel Hay (11)	49
Lauren Davies (11)	50
Brody Anderson (11)	51
Leigh Corstorphine (11)	52
Melissa Page (11)	53

Hanna Brown (11)	54
Yasmind Piatkowski (11)	55
Paul Clark (10)	56
Connor Lawrie (11)	57
Fraser Kirkman (11)	58
Ellis Wardle (11)	58

Dean Park Primary School, Balerno

Julia Green (11)	59
Hannah Fisher (11)	60
Siân Traynor (10)	61

Dundonald Primary School, Dundonald

Emma Johnston (10)	61
Nicole Hiscock (10)	62
Robbie Stevenson (10)	62
Emma Hunter (10)	63
Natasha Thomson (9)	63
Sophie Parker & Heather McDonald (10)	64
Keira Morrison (10)	64
Brandon Campbell (10)	65
Emma Moffat (9)	65
Shauna Currie (9)	66
Alan Appleby (10)	66
Jamit Gill (10)	67
Jemma Wylie (10)	67
Codi Smith (9)	68
Ellie Holland (9)	68
Rachel Graham (10)	69
Jenna Speirs (10)	69
Ewan Paton (9)	70
Marsail Hood (11)	70
Sophie Bell (11)	71
Jordan Galloway (10)	71
Caitlyn Beaton (11)	72
Jonathan Morison (10)	72
Ashley McFarland (10)	73
Gregor McNaughton (9)	73
Rachael Nicholl (10)	74

Fenwick Primary School, Fenwick

Lorna Brody (7)	74
Heather Craig (6)	74
Niamh Leslie (7)	75
Andrew Templeton (7)	75
Holly Sheeran-Hall (6)	75
Jack Reid (7)	76
Ben Wilson (6)	76
Rebecca Steele (7)	76
Cieran Malyan (7)	77
Lauryn Cameron (7)	77
Duncan Mallorie (7)	77
Jordan Muir (6)	78
Sean McElwee (7)	78
Joshua Hollinsworth (6)	78
Calum McDowall (7)	79
Niamh Thomson (7)	79
Cara Smith (6)	79
Gregor Stienlet (7)	80
Hazel Reid (7)	80
Daniel Booth (7)	80

Knoxland Primary School, Dumbarton

Bethany Troup (9)	81
Hannah Russell (9)	81
Scott Bateman (9)	81
Niamh Redler (9)	82
Robyn Proctor (8)	82
Niamh Connolly (9)	82
Mhairi Stenhouse (9)	83
Amy Cowie (9)	83
Aimee Carr (9)	84
Connor McLaughlin-Lees (9)	84
Calum Nicholson (8)	84
Kayleigh Marshall (9)	85
Caitlin Rowan (7)	85
Kelsey Fleming (9)	85
Daniel Smith (9)	86
John Harvey (8)	86
Rachel McColm (9)	86
Lewis Miller (8)	87

David Hughes (9)	87
Taylor Fleming (7)	87
Eilidh McCulloch (7)	88
Susan MacDuff (8)	88
Zoë Russell (7)	88
Stuart Jelly (8)	89
John Ward (8)	89
Calum Duncan (7)	89
Grace Smith (7)	90
David Henderson (8)	90
Graeme Kerr (8)	90
Ciara Macdonald (8)	91
Alasdair Lannigan (8)	91
Craig Walker (8)	91
Carla Knox (8)	92
Fionnbharr Marshall (8)	92
Mark McMillan (8)	92
Rachel Johnson (8)	92
Jamie Brothwood (8)	93
Jay Elder (7)	93

Longforgan Primary School, Longforgan

Murray Macdonald (8)	93
Lauren Hutton (9)	94
Lucy Stewart (8)	94
Heather Morgans (8)	95
Beth McNeish (8)	95
Ben Anderson (8)	95
Ryan Lonie (8)	96
Ryan Anderson (9)	96

Luthermuir Primary School, Laurencekirk

Melissa Rodda (8)	96
Harry Souttar (8)	97
Caitlin Park (11)	97
Calum McGuigan (9)	98
Summer Simmonds (8)	98
Abbie Farquhar (8)	99
Jack McDonald (9)	99

Alexandra Eavers (9)   100
Daniel Harper (8)   100
Jordan Mitchell (9)   101
Caera Grewar (8)   101
John Souttar (11)   101
Samuel McGuigan (9)   102
Hannah Duff (9)   102
Amber Mainland (8)   103
Sarahnatasha-Louise Freelove (8)   103
Sean Duncan (7)   104
Anna Hutchison (9)   104
Rebe Agar (7)   105

St Ninian's Primary School, Cardenden
Mark McConville (10)   105
Hayley Smith (11)   105
Jess Cassidy (11)   106
Craig Buchanan (11)   106
Amy Innes (11)   107

St Ninian's Primary School, Prestwick
Megan Lyons (10)   107
Michaela Innes (10)   108
Max Borland (10)   108
Leoni Doyle (9)   109
Dominic Iannotti (10)   109
Aaliyah Waugh (10)   110
Cecile Dodds (10)   110
Natalie Eadie (10)   111
Matthew Gowans (10)   111
Vicki Smith (9)   112
Ryan Gallacher (10)   112
Robbie McCulloch (10)   113
Paige Brennan (10)   113

Struthers Primary School, Troon
Laura Meikle (10)   114
Andrew Hinson (11)   114
Colin Martin (11)   115
Laurie Scott (11)   115

Becca Grant (8)	138
Rachel Meldrum (8)	138
Lee Armit (8)	138
Rebecca Clunie (9)	139
Sarp Mercan (8)	139
Erin Macuga (9)	139
Cameron Graham (9)	140
Stephen Gault (9)	140
Liam Brown (9)	140

Uplawmoor Primary School, Uplawmoor

Jenna Taylor (11)	141
Nicholas Clark (9)	141
Calum Philp (11)	142
Jake Rodger (10)	142
Cameron Dempster (9)	143
Lauren Purdie (10)	143
Fiona Robertson (10)	144
Megan Taylor (9)	144
Donald Erskine (11)	145
Ben Donaghue (10)	146

Whitecrook Primary School, Clydebank

Jodie Smith (9)	146
Kyle Pexton (9)	146
Ryan Devine (10)	147
Samantha McCormack (10)	147
Bethany Lynch (10)	147
Corinne Liken (10)	148
Emma Wilson (9)	148
Caitlin Glass (10)	149
William Robertson (10)	149
Becca Davidson (9)	149
Lisa Cunningham (10)	150
Catriona Crawford (10)	150
Lauren McVicar (10)	150
Graeme Cox (9)	151
Afton Stevenson (10)	151
Jacob Toland (9)	151
Rachael Brand (10)	152
Alison Warne (10)	152

Woodlands Primary School, Irvine

The Poems

Chocolate

Chocolate is a gift from Heaven,
A brown lump of tastiness.

The morning of a summer's day,
A cup of melted happiness.

The mist of sleepy joy,
A fountain of glorious sweetness.

A soft bed for a tired soul,
A meal for a hungry child.

The smell of every tasty food,
The love of all chocoholics.

A jewel of niceness,
The king of all foods.

A perfect treat for any tum,
It makes my day, yum-yum!

Becky Holt (10)
Ayton Primary School, Eyemouth

The Tower Of London

Oh the Tower of London, the Queen's grand flower,
Henry VIII gains more and more power,
We know the tragedies that go on in there,
Go on in and see your hair
As you see the ghosts who stare,
Soon you'll be flying in the air.
The Beefeaters cry as they see spirits in the sky,
Ann Boleyn's head was chopped off,
She plays around with a little moth,
Oh, the Tower of London.

Catriona Cook (9)
Ayton Primary School, Eyemouth

Puppies

Puppies, puppies everywhere,
Hang your paws up in the air,
Lift your tails up and feel the breeze,
Feel the knobbling of your knees,
Alone in the kennels, feeling sad,
When you're with me, feeling glad.

Billie Dalgleish (10)
Ayton Primary School, Eyemouth

The Writer Of This Poem
(Inspired by 'The Writer of this Poem' by Roger McGough)

The writer of this poem
Is as calm as a dog,
As funny as a bee,
As silly as a monkey,
As shy as a squirrel on a sunny day,
As loud as a car,
As round as a pancake,
As kind as a doctor
And as moody as a bull!

Celine Rutherford (11)
Ayton Primary School, Eyemouth

Men Of War

Falling down like toy soldiers,
Tanks rolling like giant boulders,
Think of the men that fight every day,
Fighting for freedom, fighting for pay,
All alone, nobody to love,
Nobody to care, nobody to hug,
We cannot bring back the dead,
But we can keep them forever inside our head.

Edward Scott (10)
Ayton Primary School, Eyemouth

World War II

(A local villager's response to evacuation)

You've changed everything.
I'm angry, jealous,
Anxious.
Why do you speak so funny?
You took my friends,
You broke the radio and I got the blame.
Mam treats you better than me.
I wish the war was over
And then you would be gone.

Caitlin Forsyth (9)
Ayton Primary School, Eyemouth

Autumn Morning

It was a frosty morning today
With damp dew on the grass
And cobwebs on the tree.
It was gloomy at the time,
And cold as well.
The spider has gone away.

Deanna Ingriselli (10)
Ayton Primary School, Eyemouth

Howling At The Empty Moon

When the night is calm,
When the moon is out,
An extraordinary sight unfolds before you.
The quickness of it is unexplainable,
It happens every full moon.
It doesn't know what it is looking for,
It's a cross between human and wolf.
It's the werewolf howling at an empty moon.

Hamish Blair (11)
Ayton Primary School, Eyemouth

The Haunted House

In the kitchen are
Open cupboards and drawers,
A cupboard full of smashed bowls and plates,
Scattered cutlery,
A cracked dish basin,
And the only sound is
The whistling winds having their way.

In the library are
Dusty pots of pencils and pens,
A dusty old desk waiting to be sat at,
Open windows propelling paper,
A portrait eyeing your every move,
And the only sound is
The wind tangled up in the trees.

In the cellar are
Out-of-date bottles of wine waiting to burst,
Dusty cobwebs stalking you all the way,
A taunting smell in the air,
A huge pile of dried out leaves crunching underfoot,
And the only sound is
Quick footsteps following a map.

In the bedroom are
Piles of crumpled paperwork,
A spider-patterned bed sheet,
A turn leather armchair,
A dressing table smothered with smashed glass,
And the only sound is
The bats screeching.

Mhairi Fairbairn (9)
Ayton Primary School, Eyemouth

Haunted

In the ballroom is
An old, broken piano playing, although nobody's there,
An old, cracked ceiling with old-fashioned patterns,
A dress hanging on the back of an old, spooky, dusty door,
An old music stand with yellow ripped paper with faded writing,
And the only sound is
An out of tune piano playing a sad song.

In the kitchen is
A sharp, rusty knife chopping up mouldy vegetables,
A sink full of cobweb-covered pots and pans,
A greasy cooker with a flame still flickering,
A stained blind blowing in the gale,
And the only sound is
The squeaking of the fridge door opening.

In the bedroom is
A wooden cot with a ripped blanket and a dusty pillow,
A battered teddy bear, dusty and ragged,
An old rocking horse covered with cobwebs,
A ragged doll with its stuffing hanging out,
And the only sound is
The crash of the shutters against the window.

In the attic is
An old, dusty suitcase full of mice,
An ancient springless mattress,
A wooden trunk full of moth-eaten clothes,
A box of destroyed Christmas decorations,
And the only sound is
The drumming of hailstones on the roof.

Ruth Minto (10)
Ayton Primary School, Eyemouth

Haunted House

In the lounge is
An old wireless still playing a tune,
An old cup of tea with skin on the top,
Old furniture with cat hairs
And the only sound is
The wireless playing a spine-chilling song.

In the bedroom is
Old bloomers lying on the bed,
An old letter lying on the desk,
A cobweb-infested picture with a heart frame,
Glasses with a broken lens and brown rims
And the only sound is a crow squawking in the distance.

In the bathroom is
Dentures in a water-filled glass,
A shower cap on the side of the bath,
A chain-flushing toilet,
Cobwebs draped over the taps,
And the only sound is
Water dripping from the ceiling.

In the kitchen is
Mouldy food on the table,
Rusty cutlery in the sink,
A cracked mug on the bench,
A creaky cupboard opening in the wind,
And the only sound is
Somebody eating something gruesome.

Alix McKone (11)
Ayton Primary School, Eyemouth

The Haunted House

In the kitchen is
A big old dusty stove,
An old pot covered with cobwebs,
An old marble board with pieces chipped out,
Old pans rattling as they fall out of a cupboard,
And the only sound is
The howling and whistling of the wind.

In the lounge is
An old leather sofa covered in white sheets,
A battered table in the corner with an old, rusted metal lamp on it,
A shabby-looking portrait watching every step you take,
And the only sound is
The door creaking.

In the bedroom is
An old four-poster bed with its sheets torn,
A hanging, shattered mirror clinging to the wall,
An old dusty dressing table with an old chair beside it,
And the only sound is
The creaking of the bed.

In the library is
An old shabby bookcase mounted with books,
An old reading table with a book lying open,
A big, grand fireplace with rotten logs in it,
And the only sound is
The banging of the shutters.

Nathan Craig (11)
Ayton Primary School, Eyemouth

World War II

My parents both dead,
Now destitute,
Forsaken,
Despondent.
Why was I saved?
To be mocked
Or feel guilty.
Maybe I was just loved
By parents who made
The greatest sacrifice.

William Fairbairn (11)
Ayton Primary School, Eyemouth

My Dreamworld

Rainbows in the sun,
They are so much fun,
Colours look like they run,
In my dreamworld.

Bunnies hoppin' all around,
Never stoppin' on the ground,
Making happy nibbling sounds
In my dreamworld.

Little girls eating sweets,
Birds begin to tweet
Where the chocolate rivers meet,
In my dreamworld.

Butterflies land on my nose,
They're like models in a pose,
This all happens when I doze
In my dreamworld!

Gillian Simpson (8)
Bargeddie Primary School, Bargeddie

My Dreamworld

Do not fear, the beginning is here,
There are lots of things to do this year.
The trees are made of chocolate, yum-yum,
Let's jump over the rainbow and have some fun.

The volcano has multi colours down its back,
It's really cool when it pops and cracks.
You should go and meet it, it's very funny,
When it shoots out lots and lots of honey.

When you're hot, got to the stream,
It's made of fizzy lime ice cream.
Don't drink too much, it may make you scream,
But that's how great it is in my dream.

Elizabeth Wildman (9)
Bargeddie Primary School, Bargeddie

Dreamworld

D olphins jumping in and out of the sea
R iding a fish through the sea
E very day eating sweets
A mazing sights all around
M oney all around
W hales swimming across the sea
O ver and over the sea I go
R ainbow all around the sea
L ovely shells all around
D reaming all night long.

Kharli McCormick (9)
Bargeddie Primary School, Bargeddie

Dreamworld

D anger and darkness lurks in the shadows
R esting in my plane I go further and further, off I go
E very river around full of chocolate
A liens all around
M y dreamworld is so cool
W ow, I can go anywhere I want
O h so dozy, all so fun and cosy
R unning dragonfish in the sky and sea
L iving skyscrapers all around
D rinking chocolate rivers tastes so good.

Ryan McCann (9)
Bargeddie Primary School, Bargeddie

Dreamworld

D reaming day after day!
R iding horses every day
E very day eating sweets
A fter school in my dreamworld
M ice are my friends
W indows there to smash
O ver and over the clouds I go
R evealing all my dreams
L ots of money everywhere I go
D reaming night after night forever.

Laura Gallacher (9)
Bargeddie Primary School, Bargeddie

Dreamworld

D ragons are so silly dancing in the night
R iding through the dark woods seeing owls
E lves are dancing around the fire
A leprechaun has the pot of gold hidden
M agic is so great, witches and wizards use it
W izards are so wise and very old
O ver the castle, ghosts and ghouls chase
R iding through the enchanted forest seeing fairies
L ovely fairies flying in the sky
D reaming is great!

Katelyn McDonald (9)
Bargeddie Primary School, Bargeddie

Dreamworld

D o come to my dreamworld because it will be fun
R each up to the snow and the snowflakes
E ach person you see, they'll laugh at your jokes
A nd Santa Claus will be pleased with you
M eet new friends and then they will play with you
W hen you are there Santa will look after you
O riginal things around here
R ound and round we go together as a team
L ike Santa, like me and the team
D on't go away from my dream.

Hayley Mitchell (9)
Bargeddie Primary School, Bargeddie

Dreamworld

D iving down beneath my feet to get some fish so we can meet
R ainbows always make me smile, make me run an extra mile
E els are cool, eels run, run, run, they make me have lots of fun
A mazing smile, amazing fish, amazing creature grant a wish
M onkey, monkey you're so cool, good at football, good at school
W hales are cool, they're always in the pool, big and strong
they always rule
O ctopuses are heavy, octopuses splash around like many-
handed clowns
R ules in my dream scare me a lot so I say I'll be back in a tick
L ovely glittery fish make me smile, they make me shiver in a
little while
D olphins are splashing, dolphins are cool, they make me go
into the pool.

Ellie Devine (8)
Bargeddie Primary School, Bargeddie

Dreamworld

In my dreamworld butterflies fly down
To the beach and round and round,
Until they land upon the ground,
Not making even a tiny sound.

In my dreamworld monkeys chat,
Jump about trees, unless they're sat.
If they are careless, they fall down flat,
Make a noise *splat! Splat! Splat!*

Sabrina Mecheti (8)
Bargeddie Primary School, Bargeddie

My Dreamworld

It's scary, happy, also funny
To see the seaweed growing money,
Also mermaids eating honey,
In my dreamworld!

Under the sea it is cold and dark
But that's the place the dogfish bark.
The kingdom there is a playful park,
That's my dreamworld!

Thomas Smart (8)
Bargeddie Primary School, Bargeddie

The Sun

The sun shines bright and hot.
The boiling sun is great to play in,
It is roasting, baking and
It can blow a very warm breeze.
Burn, burn, burn!

Jake Mitchell (7)
Blackhall Primary School, Edinburgh

The Sun

The sun is up with the clouds,
I really need my sunglasses!
Oh, I am roasting!
It's so fun in the sun!
I need some suncream.
Can I have an ice cream?

Angelica Petherick (7)
Blackhall Primary School, Edinburgh

The Sun

Hot, hot goes the sun,
Fun, fun go the children,
Frying, frying goes the sun,
Nice, nice sunbathing.

Holly Smith (7)
Blackhall Primary School, Edinburgh

The Sun

The sun is baking hot,
The sun is fun frying on the sand.
To cool me off, I go for a paddle in the sea.
Sun, sun, glorious sun.

Finlay McCutcheon (7)
Blackhall Primary School, Edinburgh

A Boiling Day

I can see the sun shining in the sky,
My feet are boiling in the sand.
I can see hot metal in the sun.
I like to sunbathe in my garden.

Hugo Keltie (7)
Blackhall Primary School, Edinburgh

The Sun

Sun, fiery sun.
Sizzling on the ground,
I'd love a cold drink.
Ooh Sun, won't you be hotter.
Sun, I love you so much.

Finn Ireland (7)
Blackhall Primary School, Edinburgh

The Sun

Ahh, a nice hot breeze,
Children playing on the beach,
Mummies bathing on the beds,
Surfers surfing in the sea,
It's a glorious, boiling sun.
It's a sizzling, frying day,
The sun is shining,
Hot, hot, hot.

Moray Arbuckle (7)
Blackhall Primary School, Edinburgh

The Sun

The sun is boiling,
Sun, glorious sun.
The sun is exciting,
Shine, shine, shine.
I will sunbathe all day.
Ah, the sun is nice,
The sun is great,
The sun is very hot,
The sun is frying,
The sun is roasting.

Beth Lindsay (7)
Blackhall Primary School, Edinburgh

The Sun

The sun is sparkling,
The sun is cool and it goes into the pool.
I'm getting really, really hot
And I'm feeling myself sweating.
The sun feels like gold.
I like the feeling of the sun.

Sarah Harris (7)
Blackhall Primary School, Edinburgh

The Sun

The sun is hot,
The sun is fiery,
It is nice.
The sun is nice to relax in.
People splashing in the water
On a sunny day.
It can be sweltering
And it can be warm.

Mark Ross (7)
Blackhall Primary School, Edinburgh

The Sun

It's a hot day,
It's a very good day
To go to the beach.
No rain or snow,
No clouds in the air,
The sun is hot, hot, hot!

Josh Murray (7)
Blackhall Primary School, Edinburgh

The Sun

It is baking hot and fun,
Shining above your head.
It is the sun.
The sun is hot,
The sun is fun,
The sun is big
And the sun is bright.

Scott Miller (7)
Blackhall Primary School, Edinburgh

A Boiling Day

I can see roasting worms!
The sun's burning!
The sun is sweltering!
I'm so warm,
Man, I'm warm.
The sun is burning.

Nelson Lissanon
Blackhall Primary School, Edinburgh

A Boiling Day

It is a boiling day,
It is very sweltering.
I am very, very hot in the sun.
It's very sunny,
Yeah, the sun is out.
I love the sun a lot.

Shawna Philipsen
Blackhall Primary School, Edinburgh

The Sun

Hot, hot, hot.
The sun comes out.
We all go outside.
We all play ball in the sun.
We all like going outside
In the sun.

Maya Coates (7)
Blackhall Primary School, Edinburgh

The Sun

If I were the sun
I would play around all day
And never go inside,
Unless it started to rain.
Sun, sun, sizzling sun,
The sun is fun and hot, ah.
Sun, sun, don't go away,
Come back another day.
The sun burns me
But the best thing is
It's the best, oh yes.

Nicola Cringean (7)
Blackhall Primary School, Edinburgh

The Sun

The sun, the sun is so, so much fun.
I love the sun, it is so hot and warm.
Sun, sun, sun, it's so much fun
And people are so hot,
So people go into a pool.

Corann Henderson (7)
Blackhall Primary School, Edinburgh

The Sun

The sun is boiling,
A nice warm breeze,
Time for lollipops,
Everyone shouts,
'Hooray!'
The sun is glorious.
Remember to put your suncream on.
So come out and play.

Stan Ashcroft (7)
Blackhall Primary School, Edinburgh

A Boiling Day

I get sweaty outside.
It is great in the sun in summer.
Yeh, it is great.

Elisabeth Meredith (6)
Blackhall Primary School, Edinburgh

The Sun

The sun is bright and sunny
And it shines in the light,
And it is hot and is
Very frying.

Craig Percy (7)
Blackhall Primary School, Edinburgh

A Boiling Day

I am warm today,
The sun is
Shining on me!
The sun is hot,
Yeh the sun's on me!

Lucie Morren
Blackhall Primary School, Edinburgh

A Boiling Day

I can see the sun shining in the sky,
It is really warm in my house.
Sun's out!
My feet are really hot on the sand.
It's boiling at the pool.

Megan Grant (7)
Blackhall Primary School, Edinburgh

A Boiling Day

I can see the sunshine,
Yeh, the sun is out.
I feel hot when the sun is shining.
I can see smoke coming up
From the ground.

Julia Laughland (7)
Blackhall Primary School, Edinburgh

The Sun

We are swimming in the sea.
My sweat is dripping down my face.
My ice cream has melted.

Tamsin Brass Brogan (7)
Blackhall Primary School, Edinburgh

A Boiling Day

The sun shines on the sea.
The sun, it shines a lot.
It is fun to play in the sun.
The sun is hot,
It's boiling hot.
It's a shining day today.

Aidan Cranna (6)
Blackhall Primary School, Edinburgh

A Boiling Day

The sand was boiling,
Today was hot.
It was sunny,
The sun was shiny.

Nathan Wilson (7)
Blackhall Primary School, Edinburgh

A Boiling Day

I can see the sun
On the sea.
I love sunny days.
I am boiling,
I can see ice cream melting.

Daniel Skiffington (7)
Blackhall Primary School, Edinburgh

Doctor Who

D aleks killing mutants in a case
O pen it up and you will see hideousness!
C arianits - alien witches!
T ARDIS - which stands for time and relative dimension in space
O ther worlds spread across the galaxy
R ose was the Doctor's assistant

W hen she got transported into a parallel universe
H urry, before the Cybermen get you!
O h wow! The fun never stops.

Christopher Mitchell (10)
Capshard Primary School, Kirkcaldy

My Family

M y mum and dad - they're the best!
Y ounger sister, Louise, very

F unny, with a cheeky smile
A insley is my big sister, she's a
M aniac sometimes but usually
I s normal. I
L ove them a lot and if
Y ou knew them you'd feel the same!

Ashley Walton (11)
Capshard Primary School, Kirkcaldy

My Best Friend

I went to Pets At Home one day
To buy a type of pig
I saw a little bunny rabbit
That needed to be adopted

The owners had rejected it
Because it nipped and scratched
But now she lives at home with me
She's never dared to dash

My rabbit, Tia, is very lively
And never goes to sleep
She's like a tiny pillow
And likes to eat my feet

One day she tried to run away
The dog missed her by an inch
She's happy and safe at home now
And I totally love her to bits.

Rebekah Bowie (10)
Capshard Primary School, Kirkcaldy

Autumn

My favourite season is finally here
And it's getting colder and colder!
The trees are becoming bare
An the birds are singing more and more!

Leaves are falling from the trees,
The beautiful sun is rising
And the leaves are going crispy,
This is what I've been waiting for!

There are bundles of red and brown leaves
Like mountains you can jump into!
Soon it will be time for fireworks,
All this means that autumn is here!

Holly Armour (11)
Capshard Primary School, Kirkcaldy

Hallowe'en

H allowe'en haunted with evil spirits
A ll day, all night
L oads of different costumes stand at your door singing songs,
                                        telling jokes

L oaded pockets filled with sweets
O range pumpkins glow in
W indows making them glow
E ach pumpkin a different face
E very door smells of candy
N aughty tricks played on Hallowe'en.

Louise Hannah (11)
Capshard Primary School, Kirkcaldy

My Dogs

My dogs are great and always very playful.
They are always happy to see you.
They run about, panting and chasing the ball
When we take them out for a walk.

When we come back from a long walk they lie down
And when they are tired, their eyes go funny.
Two different kinds but I love them the same.
Sometimes they go mad and run about the house like maniacs.
They are the best dogs in the world.

Shaun Gilmour (10)
Capshard Primary School, Kirkcaldy

Autumn Is Here

The sun shines through the red leaves,
Fireworks light the night,
A nip in the air. It's here!

Stephanie Campbell (10)
Capshard Primary School, Kirkcaldy

Dinosaurs

Dinosaurs are my favourite creatures
Although they are big and scary.

Dinosaurs come in all different shapes and sizes.
Some are big, some are tiny,
And some are the most startling I have ever seen.

In a way I am glad that dinosaurs aren't alive today,
But then again it would be cool.

I can imagine dinosaurs in my head
With big, sharp teeth getting fed.

They eat their prey really fast,
Don't go near them or they'll eat you for breakfast!

Scaly skin, must be lumpy,
Hold on, it's gonna be bumpy!

But there are still dinosaurs in the world; birds and crocodiles.
Man, I wish I had a dinosaur as a pet!

Scott Thomson (10)
Capshard Primary School, Kirkcaldy

Pokémon

P alkia would be waving its head in proudness of a battle
O h-ho flying across the sparkling blue, never-ending sky
K adabra using its psychic powers to throw enemies through
the cold and frosty air
É mplion using overwhelming rays of hydro pump to blast
enemies away
M esprit with his two friends protecting themselves from attacks
O mistar gliding through the clear blue water
N one of the Pokémon are boring because of the way they act
with their moves.

Daniel Nugent (10)
Capshard Primary School, Kirkcaldy

My Cat, Tiger

Tiger is stripy like a tiger,
But he's nowhere like the real thing.
He's loving and caring and fluffy and cute
And he thinks he's the boss and the king.

When it's quiet in the house, you hear him munching on his food,
And when it's loud, you don't hear him at all.
He has a mind of his own
And when I lift him he seems so small.

When I cuddle into him at night,
I feel as if I will never let him go.
When I stroke him I feel as if I will never stop
And that's why I love him so.

Megan Stevenson (10)
Capshard Primary School, Kirkcaldy

Scotland

The atmosphere's terrific
Inside the football ground
The fans all waiting anxiously
For Scotland to astound

Hampden jumping up and down
When Lithuania turn it around
Now we're all nervous
Like we were in Kaunas

At full time
It's 3-1 to Scotland
That's just a sign
That Scotland are the best!

Scott Binnie (10)
Capshard Primary School, Kirkcaldy

Feebi

She's seven weeks old
With a mind of her own,
She's soft and cute
And scared of the phone.

She cheers me up
When I am down,
She's so funny,
I never see her frown.

She likes a stroke
And sometimes a cuddle,
It's quite funny
When she gets in a muddle.

She plays all day
Then goes to sleep,
This is one kitten
I'll always keep.

Hannah McGowan (10)
Capshard Primary School, Kirkcaldy

Sarah

Brown glossy hair and eyes that shine,
Sometimes annoying but I don't mind.
She cheers me up, she's really fun,
My sister, Sarah, is number one!

She loves the summer, you can tell,
But she thinks winter is great as well.
Her favourite colours are purple and blue,
She loves singing and dancing too.

She loves drawing and also writing,
Sometimes at home we start fighting!
Sometimes she can be a pest
But out of sisters, she's the best!

Hannah Whyte (10)
Capshard Primary School, Kirkcaldy

Yogi, My Dog

Y ogi springs through the grass like a grasshopper,
O n rainy days he splashes through muddy puddles,
G oing on walks is always great fun,
 I n his ears he has big tangled knots.

M e and Yogi love each other,
Y ogi makes me feel cheerful and happy.

D ark nights he sometimes barks but
O nly because he is lonely and
G oing down the stairs n the morning there is always
                                            lots of excitement.

Sarah Louden (10)
Capshard Primary School, Kirkcaldy

Tommy Da Hamster

T he cutest hamster ever! Warm wool to snooze
O n. Forward flips in his two-storey house
M aking everyone that watches him giggle.
M agnificent at nibbling and also making a mess,
 Y ou think he's harmless but he bites and tickles.

Michael Duncan (10)
Capshard Primary School, Kirkcaldy

Amber

Amber is my grandma's cat
She loves to play with bottle caps
Midnight moons are time to play all night
Every time I sleep over
In the morning she comes to me
She would rather come to me than anyone else.

Amy Mearns (10)
Capshard Primary School, Kirkcaldy

Coco, My Rabbit

C oco hurt her leg. We took her to the vet.
O n the vet's table, cute little eyes staring into mine.
C oco is a cheeky rabbit, she gets annoyed at her toy.
O bey these words, you silly rabbit, don't tip your bowl.

M y Coco's in the bushes like a tiger about to pounce.
Y ou made my heart sing when I first held you, when you

R andomly started wagging your tail
A nd wiggling your nose.
B unny in the garden,
B ouncing around.
I n the house as well.
T hat rabbit! *Such a star!*

Rachel Livingston (10)
Capshard Primary School, Kirkcaldy

Shopping

Gone shopping with lots of pocket money,
Having a good laugh about something funny!
New Look, Claire's, H & M, Bay City!
We can't decide - oh what a pity!
What shall we buy is the next thing to choose,
Bags, clothes, jewellery, shoes?
Have a stop for a bite of lunch,
All we do is have a quick munch!
Then we hit the shops once more,
We will never, ever get bored!
We've shopped from eleven, it's now five o'clock!
Basically we just shop till we drop!

Georgina Coyle (11)
Cummertrees Primary School, Annan

Patience

Patience is waiting for an ancient computer to load.
Patience sounds like someone scratching a blackboard and
never stopping.
Patience feels like someone nagging you to do things you can't do.
It smells like beer and a cow.
Patience smells like a dead fox waiting to rot away.
Patience is waiting for a stink grenade to go off.

James Crichton (11)
Cummertrees Primary School, Annan

Happiness

Happiness is like shopping for shoes in your favourite shop.
It feels like dancing to your favourite song
That you haven't danced to in ages.
It sounds like fireworks going *fizz* and *bang* in the dark night sky.
It smells like strawberries oozing in chocolate.
It tastes like a milky hot chocolate on a cold winter's evening.

Jennifer Hamilton (10)
Cummertrees Primary School, Annan

Happiness

Happiness is going for a walk in the countryside.
Happiness is having a cooked breakfast.
Happiness is Scotland winning the rugby.
Happiness is eating Galaxy chocolate.
Happiness is waking up on Christmas morning.
Happiness is getting up to mischief with Niall.
Happiness is playing rugby and getting injuries.
Happiness is going on a quad at 75 miles per hour.
Happiness is playing with your dogs.
Happiness is going to bed!

Kieran Saunders (10)
Cummertrees Primary School, Annan

Football Crazy

Football, football, it's so cool,
I use my foot as a tool.
I kick my football in the net,
I love it when we get wet.
Cummertrees are going to win,
When we get out of the sin bin.
We are going to Hecklegirth School
So we can win the title and be so cool!

Connor Brown (9)
Cummertrees Primary School, Annan

Football

Football, football, it's so cool,
I'm playing football at Hecklegirth school.
Hopefully, hopefully we will win,
I'm not going to the sin bin.

My favourite team is Queen of the South,
When I go, I get some chips in my mouth.
Jim Thomson is their best player,
This will be their best year!

Andrew Watret (11)
Cummertrees Primary School, Annan

Football's Fab

Football, football, it is so cool,
I use my foot as a tool.

We are going to Hecklegirth today,
I can't wait until we play.

I am sub - hip hip hooray!
We will have a great time today.

Louise Maclean (10)
Cummertrees Primary School, Annan

Football Crazy

Football, football, it's so cool,
We're going to play at Hecklegirth School.
Captain, captain, that's what I am,
In midfield it's me and Callum.
Hopefully we will score some goals.

With your head or with your foot,
Does it matter? I'll give it a boot.

I'll drink some Lucozade to give me a boost,
I'll run up the pitch like a rocket ship, *whoosh!*

Scotland, Scotland, they're the best,
I hope they beat all the rest.
They're doing well in their league,
They've beaten Italy and Ukraine,
Their reputation is going to gain.
James McFadden and Ferguson - they're the best,
So do not mess.

Niall Goldie (11)
Cummertrees Primary School, Annan

Clothes!

Clothes, clothes, so many types,
Just to get them you have to take a hike.
All the shops, undiscovered clothes,
Just give me money, I'll come back with loads.

I'll take my friends on a shopping spree,
Every single shop will soon know me!
Shoes, jackets, tops galore!
I could shop even more and more!

I come back to my house with bags,
Chuck out all my old, ugly rags.
Put my others, packed away,
Ready to wear another day!

Mhairi Macgregor (10)
Cummertrees Primary School, Annan

Three Wishes

If I had three wishes,
I wonder what I'd do,
Would I wish for lipstick
Or a new pair of shoes?

If I had three wishes,
I'd wish for a shopping spree.
I'd buy some things for friends
And the rest would be for me.

If I had three wishes,
I'd wish I couldn't go,
But that's what I have to do,
So that's the end of the show.

But if I did have three wishes,
I wonder what I'd do,
Would I wish for chocolate,
Or an audience like you?

Abigail Christie (9)
Cummertrees Primary School, Annan

Monkey Rap

Monkeys are so cool, but they can be rude
And I could say they were cool dudes!
Monkeys eat bananas and so do I
And after all this rapping it is not a lie.

Oh no, the monkeys are getting annoyed
And all their toys are being destroyed!
But now they're in a bit of a mood
And now they want lots of food!

But now they're chucking bananas,
At least there ain't no sultanas!
They're like volcanoes, they erupt,
And now the monkeys have gone bankrupt!

Molly Adams (10)
Cummertrees Primary School, Annan

Music

Loads of music everywhere,
Loads of music in the air,
Drums, drums, beating drums,
Hear the music, here it comes.
Cymbals, cymbals *crash, crash,*
Cymbals, cymbals, *flash, flash.*
Keyboard, keyboard playing away,
Keyboard, keyboard what do you say?
Now the band have finished their song,
Now you can play all day long.

Mary Padgett (9)
Cummertrees Primary School, Annan

Cat Rap

Hey everybody, listen to me,
My cat's name is little Bree.
She is really, really small.
When you want a hug - just call.

I love to see my little cat,
That's why I am doing this rap,
But when I see her little paws,
Oh help! There are her claws.

Rachel Widdowson (9)
Cummertrees Primary School, Annan

Love

Love is a field of a million roses all in bloom.
It feels like Cupid casting a love spell.
It smells like melted Belgian chocolate in
A fountain the size of the Eiffel Tower.
Love looks like freshly-made turkey breast.
Love is heart-shaped candles gleaming in the night sky.

Fraser Bell (10)
Cummertrees Primary School, Annan

Chapelcross

C ooling towers standing tall
H oping that they won't fall
A ll four in a line
P eople come from near and far
E veryone will miss them
L ooking out for nothing now
C hapelcross, the power station
R eactors are all that's left
O h! Such a drastic fall
S topping you from standing tall
S tanding tall, 1, 2, 3, 4, *no more!*

Rebecca Hamilton (9)
Cummertrees Primary School, Annan

Happiness

Happiness is the sound of people being tickled.
Happiness smells like chocolate cooked or
Happiness smells like pizza.
Happiness is when you go on holiday.
Happiness is when you get to play outside when it is sunny.
Happiness is when you shoot a fox at night.

Robert Broatch (11)
Cummertrees Primary School, Annan

Fear

Fear is being bullied without any help or aid to go to.
It feels like darkness is closing in on you like a pitch-black night.
It looks like millions upon thousands of spiders running up your legs.
Fear looks like cold, damp woods with no exit in sight.
Fear is standing on top of the Eiffel Tower with no way down.
Fear is discovering unknown places in faraway lands.

Emily Padgett (10)
Cummertrees Primary School, Annan

Pet Rap

Cats and dogs, dogs and cats,
You can even dress them up in hats!
They are cute when they are small,
But maybe not so when they're tall.

Rabbits and parrots, parrots and rabbits,
They have the most strange habits.
Parrots can walk, walk, walk,
But their fave thing to do is talk, talk, talk.

Frogs and mice, mice and frogs,
They are petrified of great big dogs.
I just love little mice,
They just nibble on bits of rice.

Katie Dale (10)
Cummertrees Primary School, Annan

Don't Ever Stop Smiling!

If you are a person that never smiles, start
Because it's good for you and
It makes you feel good
But it also shows your lovely pearly teeth.

If you are a person that smiles 24/7 just like me
That's good because it makes you look friendly
And it means you are fully dressed
Because you are never fully dressed
Though you may wear the best,
You're never fully dressed without a smile.

Even on a bad day, stick on a smile,
Throw away that frowning face.
So stick on a smile
And make the world a happy place.

Lucy Ritchie (10)
Currie Primary School, Currie

Inventing

You must have willpower to be an inventor,
Be able to try again without getting angry,
Be able to go places new or undiscovered.

Charles Darwin in the Galapagos
Discovering new animals,
Also discovered Mirage Island,
Which is sometimes covered in water.

Albert Einstein with his $E = MC^2$
And theory with atoms and forces,
But I know how he did it.
Things popped into his head that were actually true!

Sir Isaac Newton had an apple fall on his head
And it made him go crazy -
He said the sky was falling,
But it was gravity.

And my favourite, Le Parkour,
Who invented free running.

Cade Kirk (10)
Currie Primary School, Currie

When Do You Smile?

I smile when it's Christmas time,
I smile when I get a letter in the post,
I smile when I get a phone call from a friend!

I smile when I get my photo taken,
I smile when I pose in my mirror,
I smile when I dance around the house!

I smile when I'm all giggly and can't stop laughing,
I smile when I'm at the beach on a really hot day.

When I smile my eyes light up,
When I smile I'm the happiest girl in the world.

Ronan Sinclair (10)
Currie Primary School, Currie

Driving

People race,
People clamp,
When it is very damp.

People race,
People crash
In a very big bash.

People buy,
People sell,
Big businesses fell.

People tall,
People small,
Many of them stall.

People win,
People lose,
People crash because of booze.

People race,
People clamp
When it is very damp.

Darragh Spence (10)
Currie Primary School, Currie

Just Drive

It's a sunny day so you put the roof down.
You drive through France to the French Alps.
The kids say, 'Are we there yet?'
'No,' you say.
Open road at last, freedom to just drive.
The sun is blazing down on you
So you put your foot down and let it go.
The kids say, 'Wow, what a great view.'
So whatever your car is, just drive.

Callum Johnston (10)
Currie Primary School, Currie

Workout

When you exercise it can be fun,
When you exercise you can sweat,
But most of all exercise can be exhausting.

In exercise you do all the ups,
Press ups, sit ups and chin ups,
And all those ups.

The coach can be irritating,
He can be grumpy,
But you can always rely on him
To make you work daily.

'Give me twenty!' 'Give me forty!'
Blah, blah, blah.
I wish my friends would turn up
So I can have a laugh.

Rugby, football and tennis,
All those sports
Will keep you healthy.

All I can wait for
Is to fall asleep on the couch . . .
Endlessly.

Dane Anderson (10)
Currie Primary School, Currie

Taxi Man

Taxi man drives all day,
Drives people to their destination,
Then soon drives back to the station,
Waits for another call.
When he gets one he drives away.
Soon he is driving home
And it's the end of a busy day.
But soon it's time to get up
And he has to start the day all over again.

Duncan Brown (10)
Currie Primary School, Currie

Wedding

It all started in NYC
When he asked her, 'Marry me?'
They loved each other, no more, no less,
He was happy when she said, 'Yes.'

Off to the church, that's where we're heading,
Can't possibly be late for the wedding.
They recite their vows and say 'I do',
Everyone knew they'd pull through.

Clouds floated high above,
So they knew they were in love.
Now leave the reception
Into the limo, no exceptions.

Now for the glorious honeymoon,
Please write and come back soon.
I'll miss them, that's no lie,
Oh dear, I promised I wouldn't cry.

Caitlin Summers (11)
Currie Primary School, Currie

Inventors

Inventors are good at thinking,
Although sometimes their ideas are nutty,
Like Sony, they had a good thought,
But now their PS3 score is nought!

You have to be patient, like Mr Bell,
Or smart like Thomas Edison.
Bill Gates' Microsoft was a good idea
And look where he is now!

Some inventions make you laugh,
Like the car that can spin round.
Albert Einstein said 'Let there be light!'
Or was it Edison? I hope I'm right.

Bryce Ricketts (11)
Currie Primary School, Currie

Goodbye

Goodbye old,
Hello new,
You have no more life,
Only still.

No more shouting,
No more laughing,
You're lonely
And empty.

Your paint is cracked,
Your clock has stopped,
No more chairs,
No more jolly children.

We'll miss you,
But don't look back.
We'll let you be
And let the ghosts roam free.

No more singing
And no more chanting.
You were colourful
And bright.

But we can't stay here,
You're bare
And too old,
So we have to go.

Caitlin Fraser (11)
Currie Primary School, Currie

Smile 'Cause That's The Nicest Thing To Do

I love to smile every day
'Cause it's the nicest thing to do.

Whenever I'm down and I need someone around,
My friends are there to cheer me up.

Christmas time with sparkly lights
And sledging down the hill,

Opening parcels under the tree
And eating Christmas tea, *yum!*

Summer days at the park
Or hot days at the beach,

Birthday time, getting older,
And presents, obviously.

Chocolate cake and party food,
Phone calls from the family!

Shopping trips with my friends,
Having lunch then spend, spend, spend!

Sleepovers with best friends
But not getting any sleep!

Singing and dancing, like nobody's there,
Silly moves, but with *lots* of care.

I love to smile lots and lots,
Even more than Jelly Tots!

Jessica Speake (11)
Currie Primary School, Currie

Bad Friends

When I am happy,
My friends are sad.

When I am lonely,
My friends are bad.

When I call, write, text,
They just say whatever next.

I say good luck,
They say I suck.

It is my birthday,
They couldn't care.

It is their birthday,
My life isn't fair.

I try to run,
I try to hide,

But they always catch me
From behind.

I can't sleep at night
Because tomorrow I'll feel the fright.

I feel so lonely, there's only me,
I feel as if my life's not meant to be.

Rhian Ferrigan (11)
Currie Primary School, Currie

Ode To The Old

The school is rusty,
Its life has sank,
Paint is peeling
And the walls are blank.

Can this be the school
That was bright and cheery?
Now, no pounding of feet,
The halls are dreary.

The class is silent,
No motion or sound,
Only a pen
Abandoned on the ground.

No booming teachers' voices,
Never will we find
The long-forgotten gluestick
That was left behind.

It's all been gutted out,
Only the skeleton remains,
Now it doesn't seem our school,
Now it just feels strange.

Everyone's looking forward
To the new school in store,
But there's no point in denying
The old one is no more.

Nikita Tilak (11)
Currie Primary School, Currie

Moving On

Before . . .

The chairs are swinging,
Children are making nests,
The bell is ringing,
Children are quivering for tests.

Now . . .

It's quiet and bare,
Lonely and sad,
It's time to move on.
Why is life so bad?

New school . . .

This does not feel like school,
It doesn't seem right.
I feel like a fool.
Still, it won't bite!

Lipika Chowdhury (11)
Currie Primary School, Currie

Time To Socialise

Socialising is such fun,
But I don't like it when it's done.

You can socialise in all different places,
Or even when you're packing your cases.

Sometimes you can cry,
Or even tell a little lie.

You can socialise at work or school,
Or talk about something that's really cool.

Sometimes you can cry or laugh,
Or even ask someone for their autograph.

Maybe you can see a smile in someone's eyes,
Then you know it's time to socialise.

Olivia Burgess (10)
Currie Primary School, Currie

'Bye, School

The school is empty,
Walls are bare,
There's not a desk,
Not a chair.

Taps are dripping,
Paint is peeling,
Dirty whiteboards,
No children squealing.

No more are the colours
That brighten up the school,
No more are the sounds
Of P1s being cool.

Sitting round the reading table
Seems not long ago,
Sitting at my desk,
Getting the wasp to go.

It'll be sad to leave,
But we've had a lot of fun.
I am quite excited
To move with everyone.

Valerie Cronshaw (11)
Currie Primary School, Currie

Let's Dance

I drive there in my yellow van
To the grey studio,
My hair done up nicely.
I arrive at the grey studio,
I smile and my teeth shine.
We move on the stage,
The CD player blasting.
The audience clap as we finish
And I say, 'That was everlasting.'

Victoria McCann (11)
Currie Primary School, Currie

Ode To Old School

Desks and chairs left,
The new school is cold.
Now our school
Seems really old.

Drawers empty,
Nothing there,
I wish we still
Had time to spare.

P1 seems not long ago,
And now we are about to go.
The teachers are so very kind
And soon we'll leave the class behind.

There used to be colours on the walls
And paintings hanging in the halls.
P1s singing ABC
And learning their next letter, D.

The teachers are so friendly,
They've brightened up the school.
I feel so sad to leave it
Because it's really cool!

The school holds lots of memories
Of every single day,
Having fun and playing games,
Getting our own way.

No one will forget this school,
Everyone plays by the rules.
Laughing, joking, having fun,
It's really fun for everyone!

Caitlin Treschman (10)
Currie Primary School, Currie

Things Change

There's nothing here,
It's bare and cold,
The paint is peeling,
It all seems so old.

Not a desk,
Not a chair,
There's nothing here
To fill the air.

Children are gone,
There's not a sound,
No one's here,
No laughter found.

The classrooms were cheerful,
Fun would stay,
Until it was night,
But it would soon go away.

The school would be loud
With teachers chatting,
Children having fun
And everyone learning.

Everything was colourful,
Pictures on the wall,
Constantly doing art,
But maybe that is all.

The teachers were so happy,
The young and old,
They made it fun,
There was always something good to be told.

Alix Dobbie (11)
Currie Primary School, Currie

From Old To New

There are cobwebs in the corridors,
The lights are turning on and off,
Everywhere is silent and still,
You can't even hear a single cough.

It was warm and lively,
There were people shouting and making sounds.
You could hear the footsteps at playtime
And the children counting pounds.

In Primary 1
I remember shouting my ABCs
And not liking my maths,
But I don't remember shouting my 123s.

In Primary 2
I remember having Mrs Laird.
She was funny and helpful
And she really cared.

In Primary 3
I remember doing PE
And writing my best story,
And hating tea.

In Primary 4 to 6,
I remember having a fallout with my friend
And calling out,
'Will you be my friend again?'

Primary 7 is the best so far,
I have a teacher who is funny.
She helps me out
And is good at drawing bunnies.

It is much fun
And big and long,
I am still quite sad
About the old building being gone.

Beth Sutherland (11)
Currie Primary School, Currie

Ode To The Old School

Art up no longer,
Nothing to see,
Everything is down
At the new school to be.

The nursery is lifeless,
Emotionless as well,
There isn't any laughter,
There isn't any bell.

The P1 classes are empty,
There isn't anyone there,
The chanting has all stopped,
The walls are completely bare.

The P2's colourful classroom
Is colourful no more,
The only thing is desks,
Everything's a bore.

The P3's singing has stopped,
Their pictures are all away,
Nothing in that classroom,
Hardly anything to stay.

The P4's classroom's still,
Nothing jolly about it,
Everything has moved,
Bit by bit by bit.

The P5s are happy
To be moving on,
But the P6s are sad,
Their classroom will soon be gone.

The P7s have mixed emotions,
Some feel happy, some feel sad,
Never to be in the old school again,
It's really very bad!

Rachel Hay (11)
Currie Primary School, Currie

Empty School

Everything's gone,
It's bare and cold,
Nothing is there,
The school seems so old.

It used to be colourful,
Happy and bright,
Full of people,
Bursting with light.

The infants' classroom,
Quiet, still and sad,
It looks plain, dull and boring,
Not like it had.

The classroom was noisy,
So full of toys,
The sweet sounding singing
From the girls and boys.

The gym fits right in,
There's nothing in sight,
All equipment is gone,
It doesn't seem right.

There are empty shelves,
A pencil on the floor,
The P7 classroom,
Behind the locked door.

It was full of laughter,
Cool air blew
A wide open door,
The sound travelled through.

Lauren Davies (11)
Currie Primary School, Currie

Ode To Old School

The nursery warm,
Children playing in the sand pit,
Painting pictures for teachers,
Now it's bare and cold,
No more laughing and chatting.

P1s happy, laughing, enjoying school,
Never again will we hear ABCs and 123s.

Going to assemblies,
Listening to Mrs Wood,
Playing in the playground,
Lots of injuries in P2.

P3 was a colourful class,
Bright colours and painting,
Now it's just purple, flaky walls,
An emotionless class.

P4, lots of dancing,
Playing with friends,
It's now sad and lonely,
No more dancing.

P5, a great, lively, fun, exciting class,
With lots of art on its walls,
But that's all in the past.
It's quiet and empty,
So still you could hear a pin drop.

P6, nearly P7!
Warm, even if the teachers are shouting!
It's boring now everything is gone,
Silent, you could hear a mouse.

P7, last year!
Great laughs, great teachers, good times.
Never again will there be laughs,
Now we must leave the school behind.

Brody Anderson (11)
Currie Primary School, Currie

It's All Over

The corridor floors
Are dusty and grey,
Paintings are peeling,
And fading away.

No more colours
That brighten the day,
Gone are the children
And infants that play.

A doll in the corner
That's covered in sand,
A stain on the carpet
And one rubber band.

No more singing
Or chanting their ABCs,
Their classroom is quiet
And so is P7B's.

Purple walls that have
Nearly turned black,
A dripping tap
And no going back.

School used to be fun
With rays of sun,
But I just can't face it
Now that it's gone.

Leigh Corstorphine (11)
Currie Primary School, Currie

Ode To The Old School

The walls are bare,
The air is cold,
Suddenly our school
Seems shabby and old.

The corridors are lifeless,
The classrooms are old,
And soon our school
Will be sold.

There is no smell of coffee
In the staffroom,
There is no noise
Coming from the classrooms.

The footsteps of children
Are no longer heard,
The children who made the footsteps
Are no longer here.

There is no writing
On the whiteboard,
There is no longer
A teacher to write on it.

There is no longer
Paintings hanging on the walls,
There are no more bright paintings
Hanging in the corridors.

Melissa Page (11)
Currie Primary School, Currie

Ode To The Old School

The classrooms are old,
The paint is peeling,
Cupboards are empty
And taps are dripping.

The corridors are silent,
Sad, dull and bare,
Everything seems different,
Still, everybody cares.

The big halls are quiet,
Still the same smell,
But no one's waiting
For the bell.

No more pictures
Hanging on the wall,
No more children
Having a ball.

No more playgrounds
That were always full,
But no one will forget
Our old school!

Hanna Brown (11)
Currie Primary School, Currie

Ode To The Old School

Look inside the classroom,
It's all empty and bare,
Where's the fun and laughter?
It's all gone, but where?

Go to the assembly hall,
It's all lifeless and sad,
I think about our P1 show,
And oh, I was bad.

The corridors are empty,
No teachers to give you a shout,
It's all quiet and lonely
Because no one's about.

I remember my first day, very clear,
It was filled with millions of fears,
But now I've been here a very long time,
All of my memories give me tears.

The playground gives loads of memories,
There were fallouts, fighting, crying and falling.
The playground was a joyful place,
But now the playground to say goodbye is calling.

Yasmind Piatkowski (11)
Currie Primary School, Currie

Farewell

Your walls are bare,
You are no more alive,
They are going to knock you down
But your soul will live on.

The air is cold,
You are so old,
The walls are stripped,
You are empty.

The corridors are lifeless,
There is no joy,
The children are away,
We wish we could stay.

No more will you hear music through your walls,
No more will you hear joyful children,
No more,
No more.

Paul Clark (10)
Currie Primary School, Currie

Flashbacks From School

No more music . . .
No more maths . . .
No more talking . . .
No more clashes . . .
It's bare . . .
It's dull . . .
It's gloomy . . .
It's lonely . . .
It's sad . . .
It's still . . .
It's cold . . .
I used to hear footsteps and singing,
But now I cannot.
My classroom was a friendly place,
But now it is not.
There's only one thing that it's got . . .
A door!

Connor Lawrie (11)
Currie Primary School, Currie

Memories Of School

The peeling paint,
The bare walls,
The dripping tap,
The lonely ticking clock.

The faint smell of toast,
The last cold coffee mug,
The *full* lost and found box,
The last warm milk.

The passing of notes,
The quiet whispers,
The buzzing of wasps,
The screech of chalk on a blackboard.

Time has moved on, so have we,
We have had some laughs and tears.
Time is right and we have to go,
Farewell to our old foe.

Fraser Kirkman (11)
Currie Primary School, Currie

The Old School To New

The rooms are empty,
The corridors bare,
Don't stay here
Or you'll get a right scare!

It used to be bright,
It used to be fun,
It used to be light,
Now it's not full of sun!

The new school is cool,
The new school is fun,
It used to be unfinished,
But guess what? It's done!

Ellis Wardle (11)
Currie Primary School, Currie

The Dreaded Poem

Poems are dreaded,
Whoever made them up
Should be beheaded.

I'm sorry to all those people who love poems,
But I'm certainly not a fan,
I'd rather be sitting in the sun,
Getting a tan.

Writing stories is my style,
I keep all stories in a big blue file
And write them often -
But it takes a while.

I go to Creative Writing Club
On a Monday afternoon,
But when we're going over poems,
I'm staring at the moon!

I can't write a poem,
I don't know the words
And, I'm sorry to say,
To me they sound absurd.

So take this in
And understand,
That I'm certainly not
A poetry fan!

Julia Green (11)
Doan Park Primary School, Balerno

A Splash Of Autumn!

Orange, red and yellow leaves,
Falling, falling, falling,
Crispy, crunchy on the ground,
Falling, falling, falling.

The rain starts pounding at the window,
Wet, wet, wet,
And all the worms start to visit,
Wet, wet, wet.

Frost starts coming in the air,
Freezing, freezing, freezing,
And then Jack Frost starts a-calling,
Freezing, freezing, freezing.

When the grass starts to turn crispy,
Crispy, crunchy, crispy, crunchy,
And the grass is crunchy, not just dewy,
Crispy, crunchy, crispy, crunchy.

Falling, falling, falling,
Freezing, freezing, freezing,
Crispy, crunchy, crispy, crunchy,
Wet, wet, wet.

Hannah Fisher (11)
Dean Park Primary School, Balerno

I Love Christmas

I love Christmas for so many reasons,
I think it's one of the best ever seasons.
Opening the advent calendar every morning,
I just can't wait when there's a new day dawning.
I love it when we go to the fair,
It's in Princes Street, it's great, have you been there?
All the shop windows are now Christmas themed,
It is getting much closer, so it seems.
I really love stockings and presents too,
But I am going to give also and get some for you!
I love it at night, Santa's there in his sleigh,
I'm going to meet him, maybe, some day.
That's why I love Christmas, I've given my reasons,
I love it so much. It's the best season!

Siân Traynor (10)
Dean Park Primary School, Balerno

My Dog Mac - Haiku

I have a puppy,
I love Mac so, so, so much,
He is very cute.

He likes to play lots,
He has a big scent blanket,
He sleeps all the time.

This morning we found
A great big stone in his mouth.
We took it away.

Emma Johnston (10)
Dundonald Primary School, Dundonald

Christmas And Gifts For Winter

It is winter now,
Look out of the window for snow,
It is very cold!
I do like Christmas,
Brilliant presents and gifts for Christmas.

My parents are there,
I want to open my presents.
Wake my parents up.
The snow is finally here,
Now we open our presents.

It is a great day.
I got just what I wanted.
I am so happy.
Everyone is excited,
Christmas if fun and so great.

Nicole Hiscock (10)
Dundonald Primary School, Dundonald

My Dog

He is a black Lab,
He is sometimes very bad.
He rolls in the mud.

He is twelve years old,
He is a playful doggy.
He is called Sammy.

I love him the best
Because he is the best dog.
I love him better than most.

Robbie Stevenson (10)
Dundonald Primary School, Dundonald

My Cat, Java - Haiku

Java is my cat,
He's a really funny cat.
He is black and white.

He sleeps on my bed.
Java has a funny name,
Java's a cool cat.

Java is my friend,
Java is my funny cat,
Java's a mad cat.

Java is greedy,
Java chases my dog,
Java is my cat.

Emma Hunter (10)
Dundonald Primary School, Dundonald

My Cat

Cat is very old,
Black and sleek, very cuddly and cute.
He does not like dogs a lot.

My cat wakes me up,
My cat likes food and cold milk.
He does not like light.

He is not that fun.
My dog likes to chase my cat.
He likes to sleep a lot.

He likes my baby Kitty.
My cat likes my Kitty and me.
My cat doesn't like dogs.

Natasha Thomson (9)
Dundonald Primary School, Dundonald

The Winter Weather

I love the winter weather,
The snow comes in December,
Come and go sledging,
Wrap up warm, it's cold outside!
Come and join the wintertime.

Come and go skiing,
Then we'll do some caroling,
We will have good fun.
Later we'll have pumpkin pie.
Let's put up the Christmas tree!

It's Christmas time now!
The lights are up on the lamp posts.
We'll gather round,
We will wear our Christmas hats.
That is the end of Christmas.

Sophie Parker & Heather McDonald (10)
Dundonald Primary School, Dundonald

Horses - Haiku

Horses are the best!
All animals big and small,
Horses are so cute!

Big and quite playful!
A four-legged animal!
And loves cold carrots!

Fun to ride and jump!
Very naughty, just like Wren!
Their foals are so cute!

Keira Morrison (10)
Dundonald Primary School, Dundonald

The Shooting Days

Bang goes the shotgun,
It hits the big square target.
It leaves a big hole.
Down goes the big square target,
It shatters into pieces.

Here comes round two.
Bang, fired the shotgun.
It hits the target
At such speed it knocks it over,
Hits the ground and breaks.

Here comes round three.
Bang, I fired the shotgun.
It hits a big tree,
Makes a huge hole in it,
Comes back and hits the cat.

Brandon Campbell (10)
Dundonald Primary School, Dundonald

The Elephants - Haiku

I love elephants
Because they have a long trunk.
Elephants are grey.

I love elephants,
Elephants are very big.
Elephants have tusks.

I love elephants,
I enjoy the elephants,
Elephants are great!

Emma Moffat (9)
Dundonald Primary School, Dundonald

The Runners - Haiku

As people line up,
Get ready to start running,
The big horn goes off.

Five, four, three, two, one,
The runners are running fast.
Look out, take cover.

We waited so long
To find out who came first place,
Then someone came first.

We were so happy
That person got a trophy,
It said 'great, well done.'

Shauna Currie (9)
Dundonald Primary School, Dundonald

Football - Haiku

I pull out my boots,
I pull out my coat and gloves,
I run to the park.

I pull on my boots,
I fasten gloves and shin pads,
I run on the field.

We are up two-nil,
Toot goes the final whistle.
Yes, we've won the game.

I take off my boots,
I pick up my boots and go.
Yes, we won the game.

Alan Appleby (10)
Dundonald Primary School, Dundonald

Winter's Gift

Christmas is very near,
Watch the snow go by carefully,
Write your Christmas list,
Enjoy your presents all year,
Try and go to bed early.

My presents are near,
Cover my room in tinsel,
Wake my sister up,
I go to peek at our presents,
Open half of them again.

I help my sister
Get her batteries in her gift,
I run up to my presents
And put my batteries in,
Play with my presents and help.

Jamit Gill (10)
Dundonald Primary School, Dundonald

Thumper - Haiku

I have a bunny,
She loves all vegetables,
She is very cute.

Her name is Thumper,
She has a white bushy tail,
She is cuddly.

She is my best friend,
I feed her every day.
I love my bunny.

Jemma Wylie (10)
Dundonald Primary School, Dundonald

The Bee

Is it small or big?
Bigger than the rest you see.
He's big and fat, you see.

Oh where is he?
He's over there somewhere.
Oh come on, let's go and see.

Bee, can we play?
Come on, let's go and see.
Bee, we've got to go.

Codi Smith (9)
Dundonald Primary School, Dundonald

Horses - Haiku

Horses are the best!
All animals big and small,
Horses are so cute!

Small and cuddly!
Some quite aggressive but cute,
They always kick out!

Fun to ride and jump!
Very naughty like Wren!
Their foals are so cute!

Ellie Holland (9)
Dundonald Primary School, Dundonald

My Dog - Haiku

My dog is the best,
So cute and the rest, oh yes.
And cuddly too.

His fur is so black.
He loves his squeaky snowman
To play with all day.

He loves all his baths,
Very strange for some dogs, yes,
But I love him much.

Rachel Graham (10)
Dundonald Primary School, Dundonald

Minnie, The Dog - Haiku

A wet, shiny nose,
She has loveable cute eyes,
Her name is Minnie.

Her very soft fur,
She is very rewarding,
A playful puppy.

She loves me to bits,
And Minnie is a big hit,
My very cute pup.

Jenna Speirs (10)
Dundonald Primary School, Dundonald

Weather - Haiku

Winter

Winter's very dark,
My favourite time of year,
Happy time for all.

Summer

Summer's always hot,
So hot you will want a drink,
Happy time for me.

Spring

Spring's a happy time,
Spring is the best time ever,
Close to summertime.

Ewan Paton (9)
Dundonald Primary School, Dundonald

Animals - Haiku

Lizzie

Her fur is curly.
She barks and runs in the sun,
Lizzie is the best!

Kyle

His mane looks like silk,
He stands proud under the sun,
He is my Kyle.

Tweety-Bird

His feathers are green,
He flies up into the sky.
He is away now.

Marsail Hood (11)
Dundonald Primary School, Dundonald

Seasons - Haiku

Bulbs and seeds growing
And springing into flower.
New life has begun.

It is summertime,
Flowers dancing gracefully,
Bright colours everywhere.

Starting to die down,
Rain falling from the grey sky,
Pitter-patter, plop!

Cold days come along,
Crispy white snow on the ground,
End of the cycle.

All the four seasons,
Spring, summer, autumn, winter,
They make up the year.

Sophie Bell (11)
Dundonald Primary School, Dundonald

The Football Pitch - Haiku

On the football pitch
Ronaldinho scored a goal
And they won the match.

The match was so good.
The referee hurt his leg,
It looked so, so sore.

My friends were with me.
My mum likes Ronaldinho.
It was fantastic.

Jordan Galloway (10)
Dundonald Primary School, Dundonald

What I Always Wanted

It was Christmas Eve,
We were buying the turkey.
It was the next day.
I came whooshing down the stairs
And I shouted, *'It's Christmas!'*

The presents were there,
I just had to open them.
Mum came down the stairs
And said, 'Merry Christmas, hon.'
Mum said, 'Open the presents.'

I had a dog,
She was ruby-red and tiny.
I called her Ruby.
She occasionally smiles.
It was the best Christmas yet.

Caitlyn Beaton (11)
Dundonald Primary School, Dundonald

Around The House

The tap goes drip, drip.
My dog eats my slipper,
Now my feet are cold.

Last week was sunny
So the bees made some honey
And got lots of money.

My cat had a nap,
I then listened to some rap
And that is the end.

Jonathan Morison (10)
Dundonald Primary School, Dundonald

The Winter

I love the winter,
We could go to the ice rink
Or go caroling.
We could go and build snowmen
And go to the sweetie shop.

Guess what, everyone,
It is Christmas tomorrow,
I really can't wait
Because I am with my friends
And I'm with my family.

We'll put up the tree,
Then cover it with tree lights,
And set the table.
We will eat Christmas dinner,
Then we'll shout, 'Merry Christmas!'

Ashley McFarland (10)
Dundonald Primary School, Dundonald

The Football Pitch - Haiku

On the football pitch
Ronaldinho scored a goal
And they won the match.

The match was so good,
The referee hurt his leg,
It looked so, so sore.

Ronaldinho scored,
The ball went on the net
The goal fell over.

Gregor McNaughton (9)
Dundonald Primary School, Dundonald

Nutty, The Squirrel

A big bushy tail,
It has loveable eyes,
Its name is Nutty.

She is very shy.
She climbs up all the trees
And gathers nuts.

Her very soft fur,
I really, really love her.
She is very cute.

Rachael Nicholl (10)
Dundonald Primary School, Dundonald

What Is The Sun?

The sun is a burning star.
The sun is like a ball,
It is high in the sky.
The Earth moves around the sun.
When it is sunny, it gets very hot.
I like the sun.

Lorna Brody (7)
Fenwick Primary School, Fenwick

What Is The Sun?

The sun is like a ball in the sky.
It shines through my window.
It rises around the world every day.
I watch the sun go down every night.

Heather Craig (6)
Fenwick Primary School, Fenwick

What Is The Sun?

The sun is a ball of fire in the sky.
It is a bright orange light.
It lights up one side of the world at a time.
I love the sun.

Niamh Leslie (7)
Fenwick Primary School, Fenwick

What Is The Sun?

The sun is an orange, burning star
High up in the sky.
It gives us heat and light.
The sun is very, very bright,
It shines in our windows.
I love the sun.

Andrew Templeton (7)
Fenwick Primary School, Fenwick

What Is The Sun?

The sun is a burning star,
It shines around the Earth.
It's a big shining star.
It is like a ball in the sky.
The sun gives us warm days,
It shines through my window.
I like to watch it in the sky,
It is big and very hot.

Holly Sheeran-Hall (6)
Fenwick Primary School, Fenwick

What Is The Sun?

The sun is a burning star.
The sun is big and hot.
The sun is up in the sky.
The sun is an orange ball,
It warms us up.

Jack Reid (7)
Fenwick Primary School, Fenwick

What Is The Sun?

The sun is a burning star,
It is in the solar system.
It lights up the world.
The sun is the biggest star.
I am happy when it is sunny.
Sometimes we go to the beach.
We can go outside to play.
It is orange and very hot.

Ben Wilson (6)
Fenwick Primary School, Fenwick

What Is The Sun?

The sun is a big orange ball of fire,
It is far, far away.
It keeps us warm but it is very hot.
It is so hot that sometimes it burns us.
I love the sun.

Rebecca Steele (7)
Fenwick Primary School, Fenwick

What Is The Sun?

The sun is an orange ball.
The sun lights the Earth.
The sun keeps us warm.
It makes me happy,
I love the sun.

Cieran Malyan (7)
Fenwick Primary School, Fenwick

What Is The Sun?

The sun is a burning star,
It sits in the sky.
It is very hot in the summer,
It makes me hot.
You have to drink lots of water
In the summer to keep you cool.

Lauryn Cameron (7)
Fenwick Primary School, Fenwick

What Is The Sun?

The sun is massive,
It is very bright and really hot too.
It is so big that it could swallow many Earths.
It is very far away.
It is a star that has been shining
For billions of years.

Duncan Mallorie (7)
Fenwick Primary School, Fenwick

What Is The Sun?

The sun sits in the sky,
It makes me hot.
The sun is a burning star.
The sun is a ball of fire.
The sun is bright orange.
The sun makes everyone happy.

Jordan Muir (6)
Fenwick Primary School, Fenwick

What Is The Sun?

The sun is a big orange star,
It gives us heat and light.
It shines on me.
I play in the sun.
We can go to the beach when it is sunny.
I love the sun.

Sean McElwee (7)
Fenwick Primary School, Fenwick

What Is The Sun?

The sun is a burning star,
It is in the solar system.
It shines around the Earth,
It gives us heat and light.
If we didn't have it we would die.
I love the sun.

Joshua Hollinsworth (6)
Fenwick Primary School, Fenwick

What Is The Sun?

The sun is a giant ball of fire.
The sun is orange and hot,
It gives us heat and light.
It travels around the world.
I love the sun.

Calum McDowall (7)
Fenwick Primary School, Fenwick

What Is The Sun?

The sun is a big star in the sky,
It gives us heat and light.
It is the biggest star in the world.
It shines on the Earth.
I love the sun.

Niamh Thomson (7)
Fenwick Primary School, Fenwick

What Is The Sun?

The sun is a big round ball.
On a sunny summer's day
We can go outside.
We can go for a walk.
We play in the sun,
It's fun.
I like the sun.

Cara Smith (6)
Fenwick Primary School, Fenwick

What Is The Sun?

The Earth moves around the sun
Once a year.
The sun shines through our window.
The sun is a big, hot, shining star.
I like to watch it go down every night.
I love the sun.

Gregor Stienlet (7)
Fenwick Primary School, Fenwick

What Is The Sun?

The sun is yellow.
It is high up in the sky.
It is round like a ball.
It is shiny and bright.
It shines through the window
And makes me happy.

Hazel Reid (7)
Fenwick Primary School, Fenwick

What Is The Sun?

The sun is a burning star,
It looks like a big, round ball.
It is bright orange.
It gives us heat and light.
It is high up in the sky.
It heats up the planet.
It is very, very hot.
It makes me happy.

Daniel Booth (7)
Fenwick Primary School, Fenwick

Rainbow

Red is the scent of roses that people pick
Orange is for the shining sun that makes everything grow
Yellow is for buttercups shining on my face and glittering in the sun
Green is for leaves rustling in the wind and falling from the tree
Blue is for the glistening sky and sparkling stars
Indigo is the indigo colour of the shining rainbow in the sky
Violet is the colour of the flower in a lush garden.

Bethany Troup (9)
Knoxland Primary School, Dumbarton

My Favourite Things

Challenging, exciting football games,
Cute, cuddly puppy dogs jumping around,
The relaxing sound of the ocean waves hitting the rocks,
Sweet, chew sweets sticking to your teeth,
Fun, fun friends' houses always welcoming me in,
Cool, funky hip hop music,
Delicious, delightful chocolate cake melting in my mouth.

Hannah Russell (9)
Knoxland Primary School, Dumbarton

Colours

Red fire is burning the house down, so save the people.
Orange is my favourite fruit which is so juicy.
Yellow is the bright sun that shines in our eyes.
Green is a stunning colour that everyone should like.
Blue is a bird that flies in the sky in the morning.
Violet is the girls' favourite colour that they love.
Indigo is a colour that is a pen in the tube.

Scott Bateman (9)
Knoxland Primary School, Dumbarton

Colours Of The World

Red, a fiery hot colour with darkness inside.
Orange, a sweet fruit dripping sweet juice.
Yellow, a bright, fluorescent colour that shows sweetness in you.
Green, a colour of stems of flowers.
Blue, a colour of a football team everyone cheers for.
Indigo, a colour that is very dark.
Violet, a light purple colour that is as bright as it looks.

Niamh Redler (9)
Knoxland Primary School, Dumbarton

My Favourite Things

The smell of strawberries in chocolate,
I like the fluffy feeling of my rabbit,
I like fish and chips from Silverton chippy,
My teacher, Mrs Lindsay, is very nice,
I like sleeping in my cosy bed and not getting up!
I like all sorts of fruits, like apples.

Robyn Proctor (8)
Knoxland Primary School, Dumbarton

Fairy Colours

Fairies, fairies fluttering down slowly, gently.
Fairies, fairies, orange and brown, nice and tiny.
Fairies, fairies in the air, dancing and singing all around.
Fairies, fairies over there prancing around gently.
Fairies, fairies, lovely and bright red and yellow.
Fairies, fairies, indigo and light, pretty and pink, boisterous and blue.
Fairies, fairies in their beds, cosy and snug.
Fairies, fairies, sleepyheads, lazy and quiet.

Niamh Connolly (9)
Knoxland Primary School, Dumbarton

My Favourite Things

Delicious, creamy milk chocolate cake
Melting beautifully in my mouth.
Spaghetti swirling on my plate,
In my belly wriggling like worms.
Beautiful singing and sounds from
The one and only High School Musical 2.
Strong latte swirling in my cup,
Waiting to be drunk. Smells so nice.
Bouncy, gigantic trampoline,
Bouncing so high you could almost touch the sky.
Fluffy dogs, lovely to stroke, so soft, so furry,
And their cute puppy-dog eyes.
Warm and cosy in my bed, so relaxing having a long lie-in,
Rather than getting up at 8 o'clock to get ready for school.
Fluffy strawberries taste beautiful
Chewing in my mouth.
Puffy, fluffy candyfloss vanishes in my mouth, really tasty,
But a load of sugar not good for your teeth.

Mhairi Stenhouse (9)
Knoxland Primary School, Dumbarton

Red

Red tastes of delicious strawberries which are irresistible with
ice cream.
Red sounds of sirens when the firemen are on a mission to
put a fire out.
Red smells of bright roses in my small, grassed garden.
Red feels like a twenty-chapter book.
Red looks like a Trespass fluffy coat.
It reminds me of the starving, poor and thirsty people in hot countries.

Amy Cowie (9)
Knoxland Primary School, Dumbarton

My Favourite Things

Delicious, runny, warm chocolate fudge cake
Running off the side of my plate.
Lovely sunshine, waiting for great holidays
In the bright yellow sand on the beach.
Birthday parties with my friends,
They're the best thing in my life.
Puppies are the fluffies,
Fluffy like a big cuddly bear kept safe in a box.
My friends are there for me when I am hurt
And there for me when I'm lonely.
Ponies are the ones I love,
They're soft and adorable. I go horse riding.
Carrot cake is my very thing, I love it!
But those are only a few of the things I love.

Aimee Carr (9)
Knoxland Primary School, Dumbarton

Red

Red tastes of tomatoes which are lovely in salads.
Red sounds like fire crackling in a campsite.
Red smells like roses in June.
Red feels like my red leather football.
Red looks like blood gushing from my arm.
It reminds me of pain.

Connor McLaughlin-Lees (9)
Knoxland Primary School, Dumbarton

Sadness

Sadness is like the blue sea.
Sadness feels like bursting out in tears.
Sadness sounds like people crying.
Sadness reminds me of hurting myself.

Calum Nicholson (8)
Knoxland Primary School, Dumbarton

Red

Red tastes of strawberries, sweet and juicy, irresistible with
ice cream.
Red sounds like pain when a fire crackles to ash.
Red smells of roses, perfumed and divine.
Red looks like the postman doing his rounds.
Red feels like an apple, round and firm.
It reminds me of fruit salad.

Kayleigh Marshall (9)
Knoxland Primary School, Dumbarton

Happiness

Happiness sounds like people laughing at funny jokes.
Happiness is bright yellow, like the bright sun in the sky.
Happiness tastes like a huge chocolate bar in my mouth.
Happiness smells like a beautiful summer flower.
Happiness looks like a colourful rainbow.
Happiness feels like a soft, smooth teddy.
Happiness reminds me of my holiday to Disneyland.

Caitlin Rowan (7)
Knoxland Primary School, Dumbarton

Blue

Blue tastes of miniature blueberries which are delicious and
taste of cream.
Blue sounds of the Atlantic Ocean flowing past.
Blue smells of flowers blowing in the wind.
Blue feels like you're upset.
Blue looks like the Scottish flag fluttering in the wind.
It reminds me of night.

Kelsey Fleming (9)
Knoxland Primary School, Dumbarton

Yellow

Yellow tastes of lemon which make you pull faces.
Yellow smells of paint.
Yellow sounds like a jet getting refueled.
Yellow feels like oak tree wood in a forest.
Yellow looks like the fiery sun.
It reminds me of happiness.

Daniel Smith (9)
Knoxland Primary School, Dumbarton

Yellow

Yellow tastes like a crescent moon banana.
Yellow smells of an irresistible, good, chocolate coin.
Yellow sounds like a cheery chap laughing away.
Yellow feels of a soft, cuddly Pudsey Bear.
Yellow looks like a happy sun.
It reminds me of my favourite toy train.

John Harvey (8)
Knoxland Primary School, Dumbarton

Orange

Orange tastes like pasta which is scrumptious to eat.
Orange sounds like a person pouring juice in the kitchen.
Orange smells like autumn, when the leaves fall off the trees.
Orange feels like smooth sand at the beach.
Orange looks like the burning sun.
It reminds me of nature.

Rachel McColm (9)
Knoxland Primary School, Dumbarton

Orange

Orange tastes of satsumas which are fantastic.
Orange sounds like a pencil writing on the page.
Orange smells like autumn, when leaves fall from the trees.
Orange feels like a squishy tangerine.
Orange looks like an orange carpet.
It reminds me of my holidays in the relaxing sun.

Lewis Miller (8)
Knoxland Primary School, Dumbarton

Orange

Orange tastes of tangerines which are delicious.
Orange sounds like leaves crackling under your feet.
Orange smells of autumn, when the leaves fall off the trees.
Orange feels like happy, when I feel sad.
Orange looks like the sun in summer.
It reminds me of my uncle Bobby when he died.

David Hughes (9)
Knoxland Primary School, Dumbarton

Worry

Worry is as black as a cow at night.
Worry sounds like no one speaking and no dogs barking.
Worry tastes like fresh air going in my mouth.
Worry smells like a bin full with grass.
Worry looks like people crying and screaming.
Worry reminds me of bad things that have happened.

Taylor Fleming (7)
Knoxland Primary School, Dumbarton

Worry

Worry is the kind of feeling that you haven't done something that
you should have done.
Worry sounds like the wind.
Worry tastes like a worry cake.
Worry smells like sweets.
Worry reminds me of a scary feeling in my tummy.

Eilidh McCulloch (7)
Knoxland Primary School, Dumbarton

Fear

Fear is red like the burning lava as it rushes down the volcano.
Fear tastes of cruelty to animals.
Fear smells of a witch's cauldron with burning sprouts.
Fear looks like a lion ready to pounce for prey.
Fear feels like my sister, ready to punch.
Fear reminds me of my sister.

Susan MacDuff (8)
Knoxland Primary School, Dumbarton

Worry

Worry is like the wind.
Worry is like the dark night.
Worry tastes like sick.
Worry is like my dad dancing.
Worry is scary.
Worry reminds me of being scared.

Zoë Russell (7)
Knoxland Primary School, Dumbarton

Happiness

Happiness is light as meadow flowers in summer.
Happiness is like a bowl of friendship.
Happiness is the wind in the winter.
Happiness feels like friendship.
Happiness tastes like merry animals.
Happiness reminds me of my rabbit.
Happiness is like the wind in summer.
Happiness tastes like a melting chocolate button.
Happiness reminds me of autumn leaves.

Stuart Jelly (8)
Knoxland Primary School, Dumbarton

Surprise

Surprise is the happiest thing in the world.
Surprise sounds like a volcano erupting.
Surprise tastes like tea.
Surprise smells like fire.
Surprise reminds me of going to America.

John Ward (8)
Knoxland Primary School, Dumbarton

Sadness

Sadness is like the blue sea.
Sadness sounds like water dripping.
Tears of sadness taste like salt.
Sadness smells of air.
Sadness reminds me of pools.

Calum Duncan (7)
Knoxland Primary School, Dumbarton

Hate

Hate is black like the night sky on Hallowe'en.
Hate tastes like pumpkin juice.
Hate looks like a black bat.
Hate smells like a dustbin.
Hate feels horrible.
Hate reminds me of Hallowe'en.

Grace Smith (7)
Knoxland Primary School, Dumbarton

Worry

Worry is black like a blackbird.
Worry sounds like a crow cawing on a cold autumn day.
Worry tastes like bug juice on a summer's day.
Worry smells like dirty polluted air.
Worry looks like melted rotten chocolate.
Worry feels like mushy goop.
Worry reminds me of getting in trouble.

David Henderson (8)
Knoxland Primary School, Dumbarton

Fear

Fear sounds like footsteps getting closer and closer.
Fear feels like wondering what bad things will happen.
Fear smells like sweat dripping off your face.
Fear is like scary caves and dangerous animals.
Fear reminds me of when I broke my leg.

Graeme Kerr (8)
Knoxland Primary School, Dumbarton

Sadness

Sadness is dark blue like a rainy, sad sky.
Sadness sounds like a weeping child.
Sadness tastes like the salty seawater.
Sadness smells like a rotten egg.
Sadness looks like a huge, dark, black hole.
Sadness feels like you could cry.
Sadness reminds me of my dog getting run down.

Ciara Macdonald (8)
Knoxland Primary School, Dumbarton

Fear

Fear is red like the Devil's horns.
Fear smells like the choking fumes of cigarettes.
Fear tastes like a Brussels sprout stuck in my throat.
Fear reminds me of the episode of 'Mystery Hunters',
When they hunt for a headless dancer.

Alasdair Lannigan (8)
Knoxland Primary School, Dumbarton

Fear

Fear is like you being scared of something.
Fear is black and horrible like a vampire bat.
Fear tastes like a vampire is sucking my blood.
Fear smells like a scary monster.
Fear sounds like evil Brussels sprouts.
Fear reminds me of scary people.
Fear looks like a mad zombie.

Craig Walker (8)
Knoxland Primary School, Dumbarton

Happiness

Happiness is light blue like a bright, sunny sky.
Happiness sounds like a house of joy.
Happiness tastes like a lovely, happy hippo.
Happiness reminds me of my birthday.

Carla Knox (8)
Knoxland Primary School, Dumbarton

Anger

Anger is red like a fire flowing down the volcano.
Anger sounds like the growl of a dog.
Anger smells like black smoke blowing through the air.
Anger tastes like burning-hot acid.
Anger reminds me of when I fell off the wall.

Fionnbharr Marshall (8)
Knoxland Primary School, Dumbarton

Surprise

Surprise is the colour of blue.
Surprise sounds like happiness.
Surprise reminds me of my mum and dad
Getting me my Nintendo Wii.

Mark McMillan (8)
Knoxland Primary School, Dumbarton

Surprise

Surprise is like the sky swirling around in the bright sunshine.
Surprise feels like the trees sparkling in the shade.
Surprise sounds like birds singing in the treetops.
Surprise smells like chocolate melting in my mouth.
Surprise reminds me of my mum making brownies for our dessert.

Rachel Johnson (8)
Knoxland Primary School, Dumbarton

Anger

Anger is the colour of a boiling explosion of lava.
Anger sounds like going crazy like a clown.
Anger smells like sweet sugar and melted chocolate.
Anger looks like the Devil with an evil plan.
Anger feels like smashing everything in sight.
Anger reminds me of when I was a baby.

Jamie Brothwood (8)
Knoxland Primary School, Dumbarton

Happiness

Happiness is the colour of the bright blue sky.
Happiness sounds like people laughing.
Happiness tastes like chocolate melting in your mouth.
Happiness feels like a comfy pillow.
Happiness smells like perfume.
Happiness looks like people having fun.
Happiness reminds me of Santa.

Jay Elder (7)
Knoxland Primary School, Dumbarton

My Pet Dog

M y dog is a beagle
Y ou can pat it if you want to

P uppies eat your clothes
E very dog she doesn't know she barks at
T here are gold patches on her

D ogs are fun for pets
O ther types of dogs are fun
G irl dogs have puppies.

Murray Macdonald (8)
Longforgan Primary School, Longforgan

Seasons

Spring

Spring is full of joy and happiness,
Lambs are born,
Chicks are born,
Piglets are born too.

Summer

Summer is warm,
I eat lots and lots of ice cream.
It's very hot and sunny.

Autumn

This is when leaves fall off trees.
The weather gets colder,
It gets closer to Christmas.

Winter

It's the best season.
It might snow,
You should wear warm clothes.

Lauren Hutton (9)
Longforgan Primary School, Longforgan

My Dog

My dog is cute,
My dog is wild,
She is funny.
She chases rabbits and peacocks.
She gets a really big bone every week.
When we go to the park she runs like mad.
My dog is really fun.

Lucy Stewart (8)
Longforgan Primary School, Longforgan

Winter

Winter is damp,
All around, icicles hanging on my house.
My Christmas tree is lighting up my home.
I cannot wait until Christmas.
Santa comes down the chimney.
I do not have one.
That is winter.

Heather Morgans (8)
Longforgan Primary School, Longforgan

Seasons

Seasons come and go.
There is spring, summer, autumn and winter.
In spring you can go for a swim.
Winter is cold with icicles.
Summer is hot.
In autumn, leaves fall off.

Beth McNeish (8)
Longforgan Primary School, Longforgan

Hippos

H ippos are so cute
I love hippos
P ink hippos are rare
P oor hippos have to get killed
O nly hippos can kill crocodiles
S upper is a hippo's favourite time at the zoo.

Ben Anderson (8)
Longforgan Primary School, Longforgan

Rhinos

R hinos are dangerous unless they are tame
H ere I am again, right beside rhinos
I love rhinos and I always go straight to them
N ot many people like rhinos but I think they are nice
O ver and over I want to be a keeper looking after rhinos.

Ryan Lonie (8)
Longforgan Primary School, Longforgan

Pigs

P igs have twisted tails and are smelly
I like pigs, they are the best
G igs sometimes have pigs as a mascot
S ince pigs have come into the world they have been the best.

Ryan Anderson (9)
Longforgan Primary School, Longforgan

The Magic Box

(Inspired by 'Magic Box' by Kit Wright)

I will put in my box . . .
A picture of a baby born on the 6/6/06,
A leaf of the very first tree,
The name that I was going to be called when I was born.

My box is fashioned from gold and silver
With glitter on the lid and
Silk and velvet in the corners.
Its hinges are made of steel.

Melissa Rodda (8)
Luthermuir Primary School, Laurencekirk

The Magic Box

(Inspired by 'Magic Box' by Kit Wright)

I will put in the box . . .
The hotness of a dragon's flame,
A T-rex's tooth with blood all over it,
My granny's twenty-four bangles around her wrist.

I will put in the box . . .
The colour of a woodpecker's wing,
A magpie's nest full of silver,
The noise of my dog when she cries.

I will put the box . . .
The ice age when things were just white,
The joy on people's faces when they clap,
When I get my presents for my birthday.

I will put in the box . . .
The goal that Scotland scored against France,
A bit of the gold World Cup,
The wonderful Andy Murray's tennis racket.

The box is made of
A bit of my blond hair,
A shave of my dad's beard,
The smell of hot chocolate when it's fresh.

Harry Souttar (8)
Luthermuir Primary School, Laurencekirk

Winter - Haiku

Snow soft as cotton
Melts silently on your face
Chills my cold body.

Caitlin Park (11)
Luthermuir Primary School, Laurencekirk

In My Magic Box

(Inspired by 'Magic Box' by Kit Wright)

I will put in my box . . .
A door to another universe,
A feather of a phoenix,
A scale of a dragon
And a beak of a griffin.

I will put in my box . . .
A river flowing backwards,
The mountains pointing downwards,
The sea high above.
The grass is red,
The trees are brilliant blue,
I will have a house made of cookie dough too.

My box is made with
The sales of the guardian,
The feathers of the phoenix,
The wood of an ancient oak tree.
My box has secrets in the corners,
Sights in the sides and
Dragon jaws for hinges.
That is my box.

Calum McGuigan (9)
Luthermuir Primary School, Laurencekirk

My Magic Box

(Inspired by 'Magic Box' by Kit Wright)

I will put in the box . . .
Some dogs, some cats and some toys,
My mum, dad, Ria, Sam and the school.

I will put in the box . . .
A flying saucer
And Nessie, the monster.

Summer Simmonds (8)
Luthermuir Primary School, Laurencekirk

My Magic Box

(Inspired by 'Magic Box' by Kit Wright)

I will put in my box . . .
The smell of chocolate,
The sound of roaring oceans,
The sound of my best friend's voice,
The first word I ever said,
The silk from a spider's web,
The sound of an eagle's beating wings,
A cute little alien,
A flying saucer.

My box will be made of gold,
It will have a door and windows
Made from precious stones.
Its hinges will be made of shark fins.

Abbie Farquhar (8)
Luthermuir Primary School, Laurencekirk

Magic Box

(Inspired by 'Magic Box' by Kit Wright)

I will put in my box . . .
The smell of cake,
A watch that tells the time everywhere,
A phoenix's tail feather,
A door that leads to another dimension,
A small kitten that grows instantly,
A ball that tells the future,
A magic snake that can transform,
A football that when you kick it changes colour,
A pen that has all the colours in the world,
A secret diary that opens just for me.
The box door hinges are football studs.

Jack McDonald (9)
Luthermuir Primary School, Laurencekirk

The Magic Box

(Inspired by 'Magic Box' by Kit Wright)

I will put in my box . . .
The yellowness of a cat's eye,
The wing of a flying pony,
The feel of brand new silk,
A tortoiseshell kitten that my dad won't be allergic to,
The scent of chocolate,
Sheet, my flannelette blanket I put on my pillow,
Grandma Sheila for when I am lonely,
A delightful dragon skin,
A nice crocodile that doesn't eat humans,
The bubbling of the bath tub as it starts to fill.

My box will be made of gold and silver
With diamond hinges and a ruby door.
When I open the door I will see
Caera and Anna and Klaudia
Playing my favourite game
And they will say, 'Alexandra, join in too!'

My box is cool!

Alexandra Eavers (9)
Luthermuir Primary School, Laurencekirk

Magic Box

(Inspired by 'Magic Box' by Kit Wright)

I will put in the box . . .
A pair of Ronaldo's football boots.

I will put in the box . . .
A picture of Glasgow Rangers holding the cup.

I will put in the box . . .
A picture of someone harvesting the wheat.

My box is made of cardboard.

Daniel Harper (8)
Luthermuir Primary School, Laurencekirk

The Magic Box

(Inspired by 'Magic Box' by Kit Wright)

I will put in the box . . .
A holiday at Codonas.

I will put in the box . . .
My water pistol.

I will put in the box . . .
My favourite teddy, Shaun the Sheep.

I will put in the box . . .
My favourite pillow.

Jordan Mitchell (9)
Luthermuir Primary School, Laurencekirk

The Magic Box

(Inspired by 'Magic Box' by Kit Wright)

I will put in the box . . .
My first baby tooth with the smell of toothpaste,
The sweet smell of strawberries with tasty sugar on them,
A bit of a rainbow with a tiny bit of magic,
The blue sea that sparkles in the sun,
A green leaf that is the summer.
On the outside it has diamonds with little key rings,
And on the top lid it has magic dust
That makes it magic.

Caera Grewar (8)
Luthermuir Primary School, Laurencekirk

What A Day - Haiku

The winter snow falls
Sends a shiver down your spine
Children on cloud nine.

John Souttar (11)
Luthermuir Primary School, Laurencekirk

The Magic Box

(Inspired by 'Magic Box' by Kit Wright)

I have a magic box,
It can fit big things, small things,
Short things, tall things.

I will put in the box . . .
The song of a nightingale,
The scale of a dragon
And the flame of a phoenix.

I have in the box . . .
Prince Charlie's sporran,
Dundee's armour
And James's knife.

My box is kept in the attic.
In the corner the box is there
Covered in dragon scales,
Held together with phoenix bones,
With buckles made of turtles' tails.

I'm going to travel in my box,
Go to the USA,
Then surf on the River Tay.

Samuel McGuigan (9)
Luthermuir Primary School, Laurencekirk

Limerick

There was a young girl from Akita,
Who had a lovely pet cheetah
That ran 360 miles an hour
And had such great power
It ended up in Costa Rica.

Hannah Duff (9)
Luthermuir Primary School, Laurencekirk

My Magic Box

(Inspired by 'Magic Box' by Kit Wright)

I will put into my box . . .
The scent of chocolate,
The scale of a Chinese dragon,
The sound of my friend's voice,
The sound of football fans cheering,
The sound of my dog's bark,
The sound of a fox trotting along the path,
The touch of talcum powder,
The touch of snakeskin,
A photo of my friends, Harry and Holly,
A flying saucer,
A cute alien,
The sound of roaring oceans.

My box will be made of silver,
The hinges will be made of gold
And the door will be made of rubies.

Amber Mainland (8)
Luthermuir Primary School, Laurencekirk

Harvest

Vegetables have vitamins,
Fruits are healthy too,
Potatoes growing,
Making chips,
Apples from the trees.
The moon will sparkle all over the world,
The sparkling rivers will dance around.
I hear a bell,
It is the bell of harvest.
Let's go and eat.

Sarahnatasha-Louise Freelove (8)
Luthermuir Primary School, Laurencekirk

The Magic Box

(Inspired by 'Magic Box' by Kit Wright)

I will put in my box . . .
The scent of chocolate,
King Arthur's sword,
A vulture's wing feather,
Unlimited sausages,
An alien's flying saucer,
Snake scales,
Deer's antlers.

My box is made of gold and silver and dragon scales
With ice and fire on the lid.
Within the corners are little toys.
Its hinges are big buttons.

Sean Duncan (7)
Luthermuir Primary School, Laurencekirk

The Magic Box

(Inspired by 'Magic Box' by Kit Wright)

I will put in the box . . .
A hamster and a rabbit,
My cats and my guinea pigs,
Abandoned animals with lots of love and food,
A quiet class,
A working class,
The touch of a daisy,
A good friend,
The smell of roses,
My best teacher ever.

Anna Hutchison (9)
Luthermuir Primary School, Laurencekirk

My Magic Box
(Inspired by 'Magic Box' by Kit Wright)

I will put in my box . . .
A roar of a dragon,
An alien flying saucer,
The wonderful smell of chocolate
And every different type of dog in the world.
My box will look like gold shining in the moonlight
With stars all over it.

Rebe Agar (7)
Luthermuir Primary School, Laurencekirk

Sharks

Sharks swim through the sea
as fast as can be
They smell a drop of blood and *bang!*
Their prey has been gulped
They're as blue as the sky
but they can't fly
They crunch their prey
before they say out my way.

Mark McConville (10)
St Ninian's Primary School, Cardenden

The Moon

The moon isn't just a rock,
It comes out in hard times to comfort you,
To remind you that anything is possible,
So keep your chin up and smile,
Someday your dreams may come true.

Hayley Smith (11)
St Ninian's Primary School, Cardenden

The Polar Bear

The polar bear looks like a snowball,
but as fluffy as anything.

Its paws silently walking to catch its prey,
but the silence is broken by the crackling of the snow.

Trying to protect its cub from any harm,
it hears a sound, it is a seal.

Waiting for the seal to come up,
the cub is starving, it may not go on any longer.

The seal comes up, *snap,* the mother has got it.
The polar bear continues to search for its prey in silence.

Jess Cassidy (11)
St Ninian's Primary School, Cardenden

My Amazing Motorbike

My motorbike is as fast as a cheetah
and flies around the track
I race to try and get away from the little pack
My engine is as loud as a lion's roar
and breaks up all the ground.
It is as green as grass and as white as milk
and shines like a diamond.
My motorbike is great, it is as cool as ice.
All of the other drivers in the race better think twice.

Craig Buchanan (11)
St Ninian's Primary School, Cardenden

Tenor Drum

I feel the beat of the wooden floor,
The pipes hum and the drums moan,
The crowd roars like a lion at home,
The tempo rolls on.

The vibration takes over my whole body,
My sticks swing and catches attention,
A judge reads the scores out,
It's over, we've lost but we had fun.

Amy Innes (11)
St Ninian's Primary School, Cardenden

The Mighty Sea Storm

Whoosh! Whoosh! There goes the waves crashing like thunder.
I can feel the anger in them.
It is exhilarating, almost exciting.
I am in a small boat crashing against the rocks wildly.
There is bits of wood flying off the boat rapidly
and it is a terrifying sight to see.
The sky is as black as a bat.
I can smell the seaweed coming from the air around me
almost as if it was in front of me.
There is also lightning as jagged as a fork.
Then I see a glimmer of hope sailing towards me.
It is an orange lifeboat as bright as the sun.
The waves are still spraying like a whale and roaring like a lion.
But now I know I am safe.

Megan Lyons (10)
St Ninian's Primary School, Prestwick

The Storm

There was a *bang!* and a *crash!*
Then there was a huge flash of light.
Children running and screaming and getting big frights.
The brown bark trees were falling down.
The people coming home from work - it's hard to get into
their houses.
The wind was very loud like a howling wolf.
The rain was as cold as eight ice cubes put together.
I was sitting inside watching the storm and could hear banging
and crashing.
I could see people running about and some people were
just watching out of their windows.
I could smell the bark and I could smell the dead flowers
that were flying around.
I could taste the bark, the flowers and the grass,
The lightning glowed like a beautiful shooting star.

Michaela Innes (10)
St Ninian's Primary School, Prestwick

The Storm

Out in the storm it was a remarkable sight,
You can hear the thunder banging like drums.
You can see the lightning falling down,
Like forks bobbing for apples on Hallowe'en.
You can feel the lightning hitting the ground,
You can taste the mud as the lightning strikes the ground,
You can smell burning grass like an oven overheating.
Storms are great fun!

Max Borland (10)
St Ninian's Primary School, Prestwick

The Snow Storm

On that winter's eve that terrible night it all began to go wrong.
The thunder was roaring like a lion,
Sharp, fierce whistling noises like a mouse all night long,
Snow so cold the windows were freezing over and smashing,
Snow spreading over the land and freezing,
Snow turning into rain as black as tunnels with no lights ahead,
Lightning as yellow as the sun.
It was so terrifyingly scary like vampires biting me.
When shall it stop?
Could this get any worse?
Then all of a sudden the thunder hit a tree, it snapped
and it took no control in the air, as if it was a stick.
But finally it calmed down.
The storm finally settled and everyone was glad the night
was back to normal.

Leoni Doyle (9)
St Ninian's Primary School, Prestwick

The Storm Poem

When you feel scared outside in the storm,
You can see the yellow lightning, it's as yellow as the sun.
You can even hear the howling trees swaying in the wind.
When the lightning and thunder was still there,
It was noisy like a drum roll,
Yellow like the sun and jaggy like the branches.
The wind toppling trees like skittles.
Tiles flying like paper.
Then there is quietness and the sun comes out.

Dominic Iannotti (10)
St Ninian's Primary School, Prestwick

The Wind Storm

In a village a dreadful storm is destroying it.
Lightning makes the ground shake terribly.
The wind whips the trees like a cow boy on his horse of wind.
The village people are really scared about the tornado
                                in the distance.
You can feel the dirt and leaves hitting your face
like someone is throwing stones at you
and some of the dirt goes into your mouth.
You can see the trees falling with a crash.
The clouds are as dark as ink covering the sky as grey as a ghost.
The smells in the air are different smells.
I am standing in the middle of it all as scared as a mouse
but I am happy to have seen it all.

Aaliyah Waugh (10)
St Ninian's Primary School, Prestwick

The Wind Storm

I was in my bedroom sitting by my window.
I could hear branches hitting the window like a beating drum.
I could see campers outside and their tent was getting blown away.
They were running around like mad bees
trying to stop it from blowing away.
I could also see litter flying like birds and the trees
getting lifted out the ground like sheets of paper.
I felt really scared and terrified like the storm
would break the glass and hurt me.
I could smell the dinner from downstairs like it was next to me.

Cecile Dodds (10)
St Ninian's Primary School, Prestwick

The Big Wild Storm

You can hear the storm clashing and banging
like dinosaurs erupting from the ground.
Also you can hear the bins crashing like cymbols.

You can also see the lightning smashing
against the houses of bricks.
You can also see the storm lifting up the roofs of houses
as if they were sticks.

If you are in the storm you might be as cold as a polar bear's nose
You might also be as scared as a chicken.

You can smell the smoke coming out of the chimney
as if it was candyfloss.
You can also smell ash from a burnt down house.

Natalie Eadie (10)
St Ninian's Primary School, Prestwick

The Storm Poem

The lightning bolts flashing in all directions
as fast as machine gun bullets.
A booming horrible sound as loud as a giant elephant
stomping on a metal carpet,
Spooky shadows of trees and shrubs swaying about
like demented hyenas jumping up and down.
You can hear glass smashing in the distance
like a thousand glass jars falling from the sky.
There is grass blowing in your face so hard
it is like the wind is throwing it at you.

Matthew Gowans (10)
St Ninian's Primary School, Prestwick

It's A Snow Storm

Standing in the garden hearing the storm blowing the house tops off,
In the garden the wind is like an ice cube,
Seeing the snow bouncing off the roofs and smashing windows,
Seeing the storm that is as yellow as the sun,
Standing in the freezing cold wind looking up at the grey clouds
as if it's going to snow heavier.
When I heard the snow storm bounce off the ground
I was as scared as a chicken.
The storm was like drums getting banged.

Vicki Smith (9)
St Ninian's Primary School, Prestwick

The Thunderstorm

Coming home from football training the rain
                    was bouncing off the ground.
Suddenly there was a loud bang and lightning was lashing
                    and thunder was crashing.
There were plants that were no longer there, including a small tree
                    that could've blown anywhere.
The wind was howling like a wolf and the thunder was roaring
                    like a lion.
The heating wouldn't work and it was getting as cold as ice.
No one could get to sleep for the storm with the wind
                    as loud as a horn.
It seemed to go on and on but in the morning the storm had gone.

Ryan Gallacher (10)
St Ninian's Primary School, Prestwick

The Storm

There was a big bang coming from outside
I went for a look and there was an enormous tornado
with lightning flashing around it
The tornado was like an electric whisk at top speed
Faster than a Formula One car

The rain was like a bucket of water getting thrown against the window
It was battering against the window like an angry crowd
It got harder and harder.

The thunder was like the strongest man in the world
hitting the big bass drum
The lightning was like a light flickering in different places.

Robbie McCulloch (10)
St Ninian's Primary School, Prestwick

The Storm At Sea

On that stormy night I have to say,.
I was on a cruise on holiday.
The sky? It was as black as ink with musky grey clouds curling round.
I could taste the saltiness of the sea.
The rain was like stones battering against the boat.
The wind was as deafening as wounded bears
And cold enough to freeze your tears.
Who me? I was safe and sound in my bed,
Stunned by the storm at sea.

Paige Brennan (10)
St Ninian's Primary School, Prestwick

Laura

'Ha ha you can't sing.'
'I can.'
'Can't.'
'Can.'
'Laura, don't be so nasty to your wee sister.'
'I'm not.'
'Tell the *truth.*'
'I am.'
'Laura!'
'I'm going to help Dad.'
'So am I.'
'No you're not.'
'R2!'
'Not!'
'R2!'
'Don't be so nasty to your wee sister.'
'I'm not.'
'Oh Laura!'
'What?'
'What a girl!'

Laura Meikle (10)
Struthers Primary School, Troon

Lightning

Lightning is a yellow beam
Lightning is a big huge scream
Lightning is a jagged nail
And the shock is up the scale
Lightning is a fear for all

Lightning is Heaven's rage
Hidden from the lightning cage
Everybody trembles in fear
When they hear the lightning near.

Andrew Hinson (11)
Struthers Primary School, Troon

Do Your Homework

'Do your homework!' Mum says.
'But I'm playing on my PS2,' I say.
'But you've got loads to do,' Mum says.
'So, it's easy,' I say.
'No it's not,' Mum says.
'But I like playing my PS2,' I say.
'But you get grumpy when you do it later,' Mum says.
'I don't,' I say.
'I hate homework,' I say.
'I hate doing it with you,' Mum says.
'Wait until I finish this match,' I say.
'Now!' Mum shouts.
'OK,' I say.

Colin Martin (11)
Struthers Primary School, Troon

A Friend Of This Writer

(Inspired by 'The Writer of this Poem' by Roger McGough)

The friend of this writer,
Is as pretty as pink,
As trustworthy as a diary,
She'll sometimes give me a wink!

As kind as a puppy,
As joyful as a jelly baby,
She's as clever as Einstein
And she's really quite a lady.

She's as happy as the sun,
But as clumsy as a clown,
She's so very kind,
That she'll never let you down.

(My best friend Heather)

Laurie Scott (11)
Struthers Primary School, Troon

The Friend Of This Writer

(Inspired by 'The Writer of this Poem' by Roger McGough)

The friend of this writer
Is as funny as a clown
As thick as a tree
And never has a frown

As cool as ice
As strong as steel
As sporty as me
As mad as a meal

As annoying as birds
As loud as a plane
As smart as a sum
As smooth as a lane

The friend of this writer
Is as musical as a harp
As useless as a rubber
And has a mouth like a carp.

Jack Butchart (10)
Struthers Primary School, Troon

The Friend Of This Writer

(Inspired by 'The Writer of this Poem' by Roger McGough)

The friend of this writer
Is cooler than ice,
As happy as a clown,
As fast as mice.

As loyal as a royal,
As busy as a bee,
As sporty as an athlete,
As far as can see.

As loud as a drum,
As tall as a tree,
As mad as a hatter,
As friendly as can be.

The friend of this writer,
He is my best friend
And he is always there for me
He is a unique friend.

Cameron Miller (11)
Struthers Primary School, Troon

The Friend Of This Writer

(Inspired by 'The Writer of this Poem' by Roger McGough)

The friend of this writer
Is as quick as Grease Lightning
Mad as a monkey
And sometimes quite frightening

As funny as a clown
As cool as a carrot
As clever as a scientist
As chatty as a parrot

As sharp as a spike
As happy as a teddy bear
As bright as a bulb
He'll always say yes to a dare

He's good at playing football
His hair is as spiky as a hedgehog
He has a pet rat
And he always goes for a jog!

Jason Ross (11)
Struthers Primary School, Troon

The Writer Of This Poem

(Inspired by 'The Writer of this Poem' by Roger McGough)

The writer of this poem
Is as cute as a kitten
As happy as a sunshine
And as cosy as a mitten

As quick as a cheetah
As daring as a spy
As clever as a scientist
And *never* tells a lie

As calming as a snowflake
As cheeky as can be
As pretty as a petal
As bold as a tree

As graceful as a skater
As flexible as a gymnast
As groovy as a dancer
And can write a poem really fast!

Amy Whittle (11)
Struthers Primary School, Troon

The Friend Of This Poet

(Inspired by 'The Writer of this Poem' by Roger McGough)

The friend of this poet
Is as giggly as a girl
Is as clever as an owl
And as funny as a squirrel

Is as fashionable as a superstar
As creative as can be
Is as mad as a monkey
And enjoys cheerleading like *me!*

As flexible as a band
Is as sporty as a ball
As happy as the sun
And isn't really small

She's as pretty as a diamond
As talented as a singer
She hiccups all the time
She's a very good ice skater.

Kirsty Campbell (11)
Struthers Primary School, Troon

The Writer Of This Poem

(Inspired by 'The Writer of this Poem' by Roger McGough)

The writer of this poem
Is as cool as a cat
As brave as a lion
And as soft as a mat

He's as fast as a rabbit
As funny as a clown
As tough as some steel
And he's never really down

The writer of this poem
Is as skinny as a skeleton
As strong as a wrestler
But he'll never weigh a ton!

He's as small as a hamster
He's as tricky as a fib
He likes going out jogging
And he used to wear a bib!

Eugene Duff (10)
Struthers Primary School, Troon

The Friend Of This Writer

(Inspired by 'The Writer of this Poem' by Roger McGough)

The friend of this writer
Is as cool as a fridge
As hilarious as a clown
And taller than me by a smidge

As strong as a hurricane
As clever as a tick
As spiky as a hedgehog
And rarely sick

As sporty as an athlete
As quick as a blink
As nice as a sweet
And will never sink

The friend of this writer
Comes over for tea
Will always be funny
And still has time for me.

(Cameron Watson.)

Scott Stenhouse (11)
Struthers Primary School, Troon

The Friend Of The Writer

(Inspired by 'The Writer of this Poem' by Roger McGough)

The friend of the writer
Is as shinny as a gem
As cool as ice
As proud as a peacock

As bright as the sun
As soft as a cloud
As smooth as silk
As funny as fun

As clever as a tick
As sweet as sugar
As fast as lightning
As picky as a pick

The friend of the writer
Is as lucky as can be
As lush as a lime
As nice as chocolate
As happy for you and me.

Erin Taylor (11)
Struthers Primary School, Troon

The Friend Of This Writer

(Inspired by 'The Writer of this Poem' by Roger McGough)

The friend of this writer (Romany)
Is as cute as a kitten
As small as a mouse
As quick as lightning

As clever as a professor
As cool as ice
As funny as hyenas
As sweet as spice

As happy as the sun
As loyal as a puppy dog
As fashionable as a superstar
And is as hyper as a frog

The friend of this writer
Is as bright as a bee
Is as shy as a ladybird
And as loud as can be.

Brogan Coubrough (11)
Struthers Primary School, Troon

The Friend Of This Writer

(Inspired by 'The Writer of this Poem' by Roger McGough)

The friend of this writer (Brogan)
Is as pretty as a princess
Is as clever as a professor
Is as fast as the wind

As cool as ice
As bright as a bee
As cheeky as monkeys
As tall as a tree

As funny as hyenas
As happy as the sun
As nice as chocolate
And is really, really fun

The friend of this writer
Is as loud as a drum
Is as chatty as can be
Is as calm as the sea
And is always there for me.

Romany Bilham (10)
Struthers Primary School, Troon

The Writer Of This Poem

(Inspired by 'The Writer of this Poem' by Roger McGough)

The writer of this poem
Is as nice as ice
As smart as Einstein
As quiet as mice

As talented as tap shoes
As bright as a light
As pretty as a rose
As fun as a kite

As colourful as a rainbow
As cuddly as a teddy bear
As cheerful as a Cheshire cat
And always has to care

The writer of this poem
Will always be honest and true
Be helpful, kind and caring
And be your best friend too.

Hannah Coombs (10)
Struthers Primary School, Troon

The Friend Of This Writer

(Inspired by 'The Writer of this Poem' by Roger McGough)

The friend of this writer
Is as strong as an ox
As stylish as a superstar
As clever as a fox

As humorous as a comedian
As happy as can be
As lovely as a marshmallow
As calm as the sea

As pretty as a superstar
As exciting as a roller coaster ride
As cool as ice
As soothing as the seashore tide

The friend of this writer
Is always there for you
I am a lucky human
To have her there for me too.

(Hannah C.)

Jasmine James (10)
Struthers Primary School, Troon

The Writer Of This Poem

(Inspired by 'The Writer of this Poem' by Roger McGough)

The writer of this poem
Is as pretty as a peach
As interesting as a book
And as soft as a sandy beach

As clean as a whistle
As delicate as a petal
As sporty as an athlete
And as strong as a piece of metal

As pampered as a pooch
As arty as an artist
As calm as a breeze
And as clear as mist

As colourful as a rainbow
Unique as can be
As friendly as a teddy bear
Yes it's me!

Alysha Hunter (10)
Struthers Primary School, Troon

The Friend Of The Writer

(Inspired by 'The Writer of this Poem' by Roger McGough)

The friend of the writer
Is as lazy as a pig can be
As quick as a cheetah
As pretty as a princess can be

As cool as a fridge
As thin as a lollipop stick
As clean as a chemist shop
As clever as a tick

As proud as a peacock
As small as a pea
As bright as a button
As calm as the sea

The friend of the writer
Is always there for me
Is never boring
She sticks up for me.

(Laura Meikle.)

Nicola Watson (11)
Struthers Primary School, Troon

A Friend Of This Writer

(Inspired by 'The Writer of this Poem' by Roger McGough)

A friend of this writer
Is as happy as the sun
As quick as a cheetah
And can make me have some fun

He's as friendly as a clown
As clever as my dad
As strong as a boxer
And never makes me sad

He's as artistic as a pen
As brave as a bear
As useful as my cousin
And always gives me a dare.

Jonathan Pake (11)
Struthers Primary School, Troon

The Writer Of This Poem

(Inspired by 'The Writer of this Poem' by Roger McGough)

The writer of this poem
Is as creative as a pen
Is as smart as Dr Einstein
And has been to see Big Ben

She's as dancy as Madonna
As gorgeous as a model
As lively as a light bulb
And her language is a doddle

As musical as a flute
As graceful as a skater
As loud as a car engine
But never arrives later.

Olivia Riddle (11)
Struthers Primary School, Troon

The Writer Of This Poem

(Inspired by 'The Writer of this Poem' by Roger McGough)

The writer of this poem
Is as small as a mouse
As strong as a hurricane
But has a big house.

As bright as a light
He is not a cheetah
And loves 'The Simpsons'

As curious as a cat
He really loves to rap
His favourite sport is football
He's quite a jolly chap!

Rory McAughtrie (11)
Struthers Primary School, Troon

Sounds Poem

It is quiet, I can hear
pages flicking, tills tinging,
chairs creaking, clocks ticking.

It is noisy, I can hear
people screaming, footballs banging,
People running, cars moving.

Where am I?

Findlay Cueto (8)
The Edinburgh Academy Junior School, Edinburgh

Sounds Poem

It is quiet, I can hear
the wind howling, squirrels scuttling,
birds chirping, the leaves rattling.

It is noisy, I can hear
plates clattering, people eating,
the tap running, chairs squeaking.

Where am I?

Lorne Scott-Dempster (8)
The Edinburgh Academy Junior School, Edinburgh

Sounds Poem

It is quiet, I can hear
clocks tick-tocking, fingers drumming,
scanners beeping, book shelves squeaking.

It is noisy, I can hear
children shouting, trees rustling,
balls bouncing, sports centre whirring.

Where am I?

Charlie Edward (8)
The Edinburgh Academy Junior School, Edinburgh

Sounds Poem

It is quiet, I can hear
chairs squeaking, people talking,
TV clicking, pencils scribbling.

It is noisy, I can hear
children shouting, feet stamping,
swing creaking, monkey bars clanging.

Where am I?

Seoras Russell (8)
The Edinburgh Academy Junior School, Edinburgh

Sounds Poem

It is quiet, I can hear
people reading, pages fluttering,
chairs banging and clocks ticking.

It is noisy, I can hear
children screaming and tills dinging.

Where am I?

Cameron Mellis (7)
The Edinburgh Academy Junior School, Edinburgh

Sounds Poem

It is quiet, I can hear
the swings squeaking, people talking,
trees squeaking, gates creaking.

It is noisy, I can hear
tiles clattering, wind blowing,
leaves rustling and the people shouting.

Where am I?

Charlie Thompson (8)
The Edinburgh Academy Junior School, Edinburgh

Sounds Poem

It is quiet, I can hear
birds chirping, leaves crackling,
twigs snapping, grass swaying.

It is noisy, I can hear
children shouting, wind howling,
bells ringing, whistles blowing.

Where am I?

Matthew Black (8)
The Edinburgh Academy Junior School, Edinburgh

Sounds Poem

It is quiet, I can hear
people walking, birds chirping,
trees swishing, kittens miaowing.

It is noisy, I can hear
cars accelerating, trees howling,
people shouting, bars rattling.

Where am I?

Henry Hunter (8)
The Edinburgh Academy Junior School, Edinburgh

Sounds Poem

It is quiet, I can hear
people chattering, wind whistling,
feet walking, bees buzzing.

It is noisy, I can hear
children screaming, machines humming,
cash tinkling, water splashing.

Where am I?

Jamie Carson (8)
The Edinburgh Academy Junior School, Edinburgh

Sounds Poem

It is quiet, I can hear
oven ringing, microwave pinging,
radio singing, fridge humming.

It is noisy, I can hear
toilets flushing, bath gurgling,
sink running, shaving foam spraying.

What am I?

Jonathan Hannah (8)
The Edinburgh Academy Junior School, Edinburgh

Sounds Poem

It is quiet, I can hear
pipes gargling, water splashing,
a fly buzzing, myself breathing.

It is noisy, I can hear
fans chanting, whistles blowing,
feet stomping, balls getting whacked.

Where am I?

Samuel Brailsford (8)
The Edinburgh Academy Junior School, Edinburgh

Sounds Poem

It is quiet, I can hear
chairs squeaking, pages rattling,
beds flapping, clocks ticking.

It is noisy, I can hear
children screaming, people leaving,
ride rattling, money rattling.

Where am I?

Azim Ghafoor (8)
The Edinburgh Academy Junior School, Edinburgh

Sounds Poem

It is quiet, I can hear
doors creaking, heart beating,
books swishing, breath panting.

It is noisy, I can hear
fighters roaring, blades crashing,
warriors crying in pain, chariots clicking.

Where am I?

Yann McLatchie (8)
The Edinburgh Academy Junior School, Edinburgh

Sounds Poem

It is quiet, I can hear
clocks ticking, books opening,
chairs squeaking, pages flapping.

It is quiet, I can hear
explosions exploding, experiments hissing,
children chatting, glass smashing.

Where am I?

Michael Olsen (8)
The Edinburgh Academy Junior School, Edinburgh

Sounds Poem

It is quiet, I can hear
bees buzzing, things falling,
clocks clicking, wind blowing.

It is noisy, I can hear
people laughing, people splashing,
people screaming, bubbles bobbing.

Where am I?

Jean-Claude Houbert (8)
The Edinburgh Academy Junior School, Edinburgh

Rockets

Jets of colour, what a sight
Wait for a rocket to take flight
Flying in space
Rockets - red, yellow, blue, green, purple, pink, gold and silver
Just like a dream rocks fly
Rockets soar, rockets glide
Rockets.

Cameron Bennett (8)
Toronto Primary School, Livingston

Hallowe'en Night

H airy spiders on the door,
A pple dunking in the night,
L izzie the witch on a broomstick,
L anterns everywhere,
O h what a fright!
W hite ghosts everywhere,
E ven fog's coming in,
E erie dark alleyways,
N icker picker is sneaking around.

Rebecca Picken (8)
Toronto Primary School, Livingston

Peace

Peace is ocean-blue.
Peace tastes like a huge apple pie.
It smells like a glowing, sweet, yellow daffodil.
It looks like a graceful moving dolphin.
Peace sounds quiet and joyful.
Peace feels like sleek moving waves.

Zara Nicol (9)
Toronto Primary School, Livingston

Lions

L ive in the Savannah
I think they're cool
O ther predators will try and take over the pride
N ever give up their territory
S harp teeth help to eat their food.

Kyle McCabe (8)
Toronto Primary School, Livingston

Hallowe'en

H airy bugs in the night,
A ll the adults get a fright,
L ots of pumpkins on the doorstep,
L ots of witches, vampires and more they'll be at your door,
O h what a fright!
W hen it's time for the bats we all scream,
E veryone is scared now,
E ating your sweets at home
N ow you have a knock on the door.

Becca Grant (8)
Toronto Primary School, Livingston

Hallowe'en Poem

H airy bats flying in the night,
A ll the children running about,
L ots of pumpkins at your service,
L ots of vampires laughing out loud,
O h what a fright!
W e will close the witches' door but they'll come back for more,
E ven black cats come out,
E ven bats,
N ever coming out for Hallowe'en again.

Rachel Meldrum (8)
Toronto Primary School, Livingston

Owls

O n Sunday I played with my bird
W ild animals fly quickly
L et's let them go
S cottish people are good at flying birds.

Lee Armit (8)
Toronto Primary School, Livingston

Fireworks

F antastic colours, watch them fly up in the sky,
I ndigo, violet, blue and red, watch them fly above your head,
R eally loud noises, cover your ears,
E xploding, booming, crashing, high flying, high, high, high,
W onderful colours sprinkled everywhere, very high up in the air,
O range, luminous green as well, enough colours to fill a well,
R ambunctious red running everywhere, exploding high
                                                  above our hair,
K *aboom!* Crashing exploding away, very, very way up high,
S oaring high to the sky till they explode way up high.

Rebecca Clunie (9)
Toronto Primary School, Livingston

Anger

Anger is blood-red.
It tastes like fifty hard bricks.
It smells like a dustbin.
It looks like a crackling flame.
It sounds like a thousand corpses marching in a continuous beat.
Anger is fierce.

Sarp Mercan (8)
Toronto Primary School, Livingston

Peace

Peace is like a light peach.
It tastes like a lovely baked apple pie.
Peace smells like a burning scented candle.
Peace looks like a moving blue sea.
It sounds like a sweet bird singing.
Peace is calm and bright.

Erin Macuga (9)
Toronto Primary School, Livingston

Basketball

B e the ball,
A very big throw,
S core lots of points,
K eep your eye on the ball,
E ye always on the ball,
T hrow with skill in the hoop,
B asketball is about the crowd,
A lways trick your enemy,
L ove being the champ,
L ove having skill.

Cameron Graham (9)
Toronto Primary School, Livingston

Anger

Anger is ultra dark red.
It tastes like a burning fire with black ashes of coal.
Anger looks like a big bad Devil.
The sound of evil laughs, the horrid laughs
Made by a one-hundred-year-old witch cooking up a spell.
Anger is horrible.

Stephen Gault (9)
Toronto Primary School, Livingston

Anger

Anger is red-hot
It tastes like a flaming hot chilli pepper burning
And popping in my mouth
It smells like a bonfire
It looks like a bomb exploding
It sounds like a chainsaw going off in my head
It feels like my blood is boiling.

Liam Brown (9)
Toronto Primary School, Livingston

HOYS - Horse Of The Year Show

HOYS
Six am
Getting ready
HOYS
Nine am
Horse primping
HOYS
Twelve noon
Show class starting
HOYS
Twelve-thirty pm
Class still going
HOYS
One pm
Class finished
HOYS
Three pm
About to leave
HOYS.

Jenna Taylor (11)
Uplawmoor Primary School, Uplawmoor

Hallowe'en

H aunted hats on horrible heads,
A s action-packed mummies go to see Fred,
L uminous ghosts try to scare Ed,
L ucky Dracula finds a kill,
O ld Mr Dracula realised it was Bill!
W ho had killed old Mr Bill on that hill?
E vil devils rule down below,
E lectric robots dance all night,
N asty goblins will try to give you a fright!

Nicholas Clark (9)
Uplawmoor Primary School, Uplawmoor

My Sister Nichola

M y sister is called Nichola,
Y ou'd really like to meet her.

S he plays the piano and the flute,
I am annoying to her.
S he is very good in school.
T he teachers think she's fine.
E very dog likes a pet from her.
R ight is what she is all the time.

N ice, is what she is also,
I am usually nice back.
C offee is what she sometimes drinks,
H allowe'en ideas, she doesn't lack,
O verall she is a very good sister,
L ovely and kind always
A nd that is my sister, Nichola.

Calum Philp (11)
Uplawmoor Primary School, Uplawmoor

Hallowe'en

H orror lurks in every corner
A ction Men and Freddy Krugers
L ollipops in trick or treat bags
L ovely costumes, others bad
O wls hooting
W ee ones scared
E lderly snooping
E veryone is having fun
N ot a soul is not!

Jake Rodger (10)
Uplawmoor Primary School, Uplawmoor

Sisters

Sisters
In the dining room on Monday
Always eating
Sisters
In the lounge on Tuesday
Always changing channels
Sisters
In their room on Wednesday
Always playing music loudly
Sisters
On the computer on Thursday
Always playing baby games
Sisters
In my room on Friday
Always being annoying
Sisters
Outside at the wall speaking to their friend on Saturday
Always chatting
Sisters
In their bed on Sunday
Always snoring
Sisters.

Cameron Dempster (9)
Uplawmoor Primary School, Uplawmoor

Weather

W eather can be wet
E gypt can be hot!
A nyway I like warm
T he desert I like not!
H eat turns my hair blonde
E ven to the fringe
R ain is falling down
S oon it will be wet.

Lauren Purdie (10)
Uplawmoor Primary School, Uplawmoor

My Pony Candy

M ad about galloping
Y oung hearted

P otty
O ats and grass
N uts about jumping
Y awn, she does that a lot

C heeky, cute and cuddly
A mazing in every way
N oisy eater
D arling eyes
Y ou might be fooled, I was!

Fiona Robertson (10)
Uplawmoor Primary School, Uplawmoor

Horses

Sassy entrants
All colours
Always galloping
Running free
Gigantic jumpers
Fantastic foals
Moody mares
Gentle geldings
Stressed stallions.

Megan Taylor (9)
Uplawmoor Primary School, Uplawmoor

My Family

My brother is quite cool
And he works really hard at school.
He likes to play all through the day,
Especially in the month of May.
Even though he can be a pest,
I think he is the best.

My sister has a great mind
And she is very kind.
She has good fashion sense,
Even though she can talk nonsense.
She can be a bit of a pest,
But I think she is the best.

My mum is very nice
And she cooks a good curry and rice.
She keeps the house clean
And her first name is Jean.
Sometimes Mum's a bit of a pest,
But I think she is the best.

My dad is the boss man
And he drives a silver van.
He works hard all the time,
But he likes to relax with a glass of wine.
Sometimes my dad can be a pest,
But I think he is the best.

My family can be a pest,
But I think they are simply the best.

Donald Erskine (11)
Uplawmoor Primary School, Uplawmoor

Brothers

B arking mad
R eally annoying
O therwise crazy
T otally bugs me
H ave taken my gloves
E ver so dim
R arely smart
S till OK, because I'm stuck with them.

Ben Donaghue (10)
Uplawmoor Primary School, Uplawmoor

A Friend

With friends you can play, having lots of fun,
With friends you can also laugh and run.

My friends and I like to play outside,
Sometimes on our bikes we go for a ride.

My friends and I sometimes go swimming,
Cayden, my friend, is as light as a feather.

So if you feel lonely, just call your friend,
If they are good they will be there till the end.

Jodie Smith (9)
Whitecrook Primary School, Clydebank

Good Friends

F riends are so good to you,
R elationships are strong too,
I n-between friends is where I belong,
E very day we play along,
N o matter, rain or shine,
D aytime, night-time, any time,
S ure it's good to have friends like mine.

Kyle Pexton (9)
Whitecrook Primary School, Clydebank

Special People

Friends are special people,
You play with them a lot.

Friends should never fall out,
They are nice to have about.

Friends are always there,
In happy times and sad.

Even when times get really bad,
I am glad that I have friends.

Ryan Devine (10)
Whitecrook Primary School, Clydebank

Heavenly Friends

Here are my friends with eyes like jewels,
Straight from Heaven to play with me.

Have a guess who my friends are?
Yes, it's you!
So thank you for being my friend.

I know our friendship will never end,
Especially as they are my heavenly friends.

Samantha McCormack (10)
Whitecrook Primary School, Clydebank

Lots Of Friends

I have lots of friends who are really cool,
I play with them when I come home from school.

When I feel lonely or sad,
I talk to my friends and things don't seem so bad.

Always and forever best of friends
They can count on me to be there for them.

Bethany Lynch (10)
Whitecrook Primary School, Clydebank

Best Friends Forever

Luckily I have a best friend,
Our friendship will never end.
Unfortunately we disagree,
But that's the difference
Between my friend and me.
Surprisingly we're not the same,
However she likes me and I like her.
Although when our work is done
We tend to have some time for fun.
Through good and bad we are together
Knowing we will always be
Best friends forever!
Playing together, eating lunch,
Is that how you describe friends too?

Corinne Liken (10)
Whitecrook Primary School, Clydebank

Fabulous Friends

Fabulous friends are all you need,
Some may be tall while others are small,
But we play in shine and fall,
Kicking the ball and playing netball,
We sometimes fight but then we remember
All the fun times we had together
So we are best friends forever . . .

The teacher calls us the mad three!
My mum said, 'I do not disagree.'
Even though we are the mad three
We are kind and helpful for everyone to see.

Emma Wilson (9)
Whitecrook Primary School, Clydebank

A Friend

F urious things that friends may say,
R inging doorbells every day.
I nside houses where sleepovers take place.
E ntering houses and laughing together,
N ever wanting to fall out.
D on't hold grudges with each other,
S ecret sharing all together.

Caitlin Glass (10)
Whitecrook Primary School, Clydebank

My Best Friend

Kyle and I will play every day,
At school we like to play football,
Being chased by the girls is lots of fun,
Annoying them is even better,
Doing all sorts of things together,
With my best friend.

William Robertson (10)
Whitecrook Primary School, Clydebank

My Friends

My friends at school,
My friends at home.

Friends here, friends there,
My friends are everywhere.

All my friends are fun,
Kind, gentle, cheerful.

Yes, my friends are everywhere!

Becca Davidson (9)
Whitecrook Primary School, Clydebank

Always Friends

Friends are important people, you can depend on,
Friends are there for you in good times or bad.

Sometimes you may have arguments,
Which can lead to friends taking sides,
Or being stuck in the middle.

Just remember your friends and you,
May not get on right now.
Then think back and remember the saying:
'Once friends, always friends'.

Lisa Cunningham (10)
Whitecrook Primary School, Clydebank

Friends

Friends are people,
Trustworthy people,
People that will stick up for you,
And never let you down,
They look after you,
When you are hurt or scared,
No matter what they say or do,
They will always be your friend.

Catriona Crawford (10)
Whitecrook Primary School, Clydebank

Many Friends

I have many best friends
They are all very kind to me,
Always there for me,
Cheering me up when I am down.
I have many best friends.

Lauren McVicar (10)
Whitecrook Primary School, Clydebank

My Friend

My friend is as soft as butter,
Some people call her a crazy nutter.

Although she has a few other friends,
Our friendship will never end.

We play footie in my backyard,
She can kick the ball a couple of yards!

So here my friends I say again,
Pip, pip, cheerio! I hope to see you again.

Graeme Cox (9)
Whitecrook Primary School, Clydebank

My Best Friend

My best friend's name is Emma,
We sometimes think the same,
I'll be thinking of her,
Then she'll call out my name.
We run away together,
To play a silly game,
If she falls to the ground,
I will feel her pain.

Afton Stevenson (10)
Whitecrook Primary School, Clydebank

Fortunate Friend

Fortunately, you are my best friend,
The best in the whole wide world.
When I'm feeling blue,
You know exactly what to do.
Bringing me happiness and cheer,
Just by being near.
My fortunate friend.

Jacob Toland (9)
Whitecrook Primary School, Clydebank

Making Friends

Friends are hard to make,
Making a new one
Your nerves begin to shake.
When you meet a good one,
They can be lots of fun.
Nevertheless they can be bad,
Which can either make you sad or mad.
However sometimes they are silly,
Which makes you laugh
It is fun making friends.

Rachael Brand (10)
Whitecrook Primary School, Clydebank

What Do Friends Do?

Friends will play with you
And talk to you too.
They help you with your work,
That's what friends do.
They cheer you up,
When you are down,
Always around if you're upset,
Your trustworthy friend.

Alison Warne (10)
Whitecrook Primary School, Clydebank

I Wish

I wish my sister was on a different planet,
I wish my best friend had not moved to England,
I wish my mum and my sister Jenifer would make up,
I wish I had seven rats and a pet mouse,
I wish my niece Chloe would stop hitting me!

Laura McGunigal (9)
Woodlands Primary School, Irvine

Memories

One, my dad left to join the Army,
Two, my first words and starting to walk a bit unsteady,
Three, my first little bicycle, it was blue,
Four, I started school and made new friends,
Five, enjoyed playing on my own computer,
Six, jumping high on my new trampoline,
Seven, my dad took me on a fishing trip and we caught a fish,
Eight, canoeing for nine miles down a river,
Nine, was a pageboy at my uncle's wedding,
Ten, had a wonderful holiday in France for ten days.

Caelum Jameson (10)
Woodlands Primary School, Irvine

Memories

One, I went swimming with my mum and dad,
Two, wanting my dummy and I got a little bike to ride,
Three, I got a lovely swinging cot for my dolls,
Four, I bought a goldfish named Fudge,
Five, my dad taught me to ride a big bike,
Six, I jumped and jumped on my mini trampoline,
Seven, tried skating at the Magnum ice rink,
Eight, I visited Deep Sea World with my gran,
Nine, had fun at Edinburgh Zoo and Blair Drummond Safari Park,
Ten, I've been to M & Ms five times, and it's great.

Holly Affleck (10)
Woodlands Primary School, Irvine

Memories

One, photos of my first tooth which had grown in,
Two, had learned how to say Mama and Dada,
Three, I was walking and running around,
Four, rode my tricycle up and down the path,
Five, was given my first two-wheeled bike, it was fun,
Six, playing on my PlayStation 1 with my brother,
Seven, learned how to ride my bike with two wheels,
Eight, my first mountain bike with thick tyres,
Learning to play a game of golf at nine.

Alistair McKeen (9)
Woodlands Primary School, Irvine

Young Writers Information

We hope you have enjoyed reading this book - and that you will continue to enjoy it in the coming years.

If you like reading and writing poetry drop us a line, or give us a call, and we'll send you a free information pack.

Alternatively if you would like to order further copies of this book or any of our other titles, then please give us a call or log onto our website at www.youngwriters.co.uk

**Young Writers Information
Remus House
Coltsfoot Drive
Peterborough
PE2 9JX**

(01733) 890066